MECHANICAL

Discipline-Specific Review for the FE/EIT Exam

Michel Saad, PhD, PE
with Michael R. Lindeburg, PE

Professional Publications, Inc.
Belmont, California

Production Manager: Aline Sullivan Magee
Copy Editor: Jessica R. Whitney-Holden
Book Designer: Charles P. Oey
Typesetter: Cathy Schrott
Illustrator: Yvonne M. Sartain
Proofreader: Mia Laurence
Cover Designer: Charles P. Oey

MECHANICAL DISCIPLINE-SPECIFIC REVIEW FOR THE FE/EIT EXAM

Printed in the United States of America

Professional Publications, Inc.
1250 Fifth Avenue, Belmont, CA 94002
(415) 593-9119
www.ppi2pass.com

Current printing of this edition: 1

Library of Congress Cataloging-in-Publication Data
Saad, Michel R., 1927–
    Mechanical discipline-specific review for the FE/EIT exam / Michel
  Saad with Michael R. Lindeburg.
       p.   cm.
    ISBN 1-888577-19-3
    1. Engineering--United States--Examinations--Study guides.
  2. Mechanical engineering--United States--Examinations--Study
  guides. 3. Engineering--Problems, exercises, etc. 4. Engineers--
  Certification--United States. I. Lindeburg, Michael R.
  II. Title.
  TA159.S23   1997
  621'.076--dc21   97-13363
                                                       CIP

Table of Contents

Preface and Acknowledgments

This book is one in a series of five that is intended for engineers and students who are taking the engineering discipline-specific (DS) afternoon portion of the Fundamentals of Engineering (FE) exam.

The topics covered in the DS afternoon FE exams are completely different from the topics covered in the morning portion of the FE exam. Since this book only covers one discipline-specific exam, it really addresses only half of the FE exam, and even then, only one specific discipline.

The format of the FE exam, formerly known as the EIT (Engineer-In-Training) exam, changed in October 1996. I waited until after that first new exam to design this book so that comments from examinees could be incorporated into the content. Guidance from these examinees helped me understand an exam format that is, even yet, still in its infancy.

This book consolidates 120 practical review problems, covering all of the discipline-specific exam topics. The practice problems include full solutions. The topics are presented in essentially the same sequence followed by the NCEES' *Fundamentals of Engineering (FE) Discipline Specific Reference Handbook*, the only reference book permitted in the exam.

The problems in this book were developed by Michel Saad, PhD, PE, following the format, style, subject breakdown, and guidelines that I provided.

In designing this book, I used the NCEES *Fundamentals of Engineering (FE) Discipline Specific Reference Handbook* and the breakdown of problem types published by NCEES. However, as with most standardized tests, there is no guarantee that any specific problem type will be encountered. It is expected that minor variations in problem content will occur from exam to exam.

As with all of Professional Publications' books, the problems in this book are original and have been ethically derived. Although examinee feedback was used to determine its content, this book contains problems that are only *like* those that are on the exam. There are no actual exam problems in this book.

This book was designed to complement my *EIT Review Manual*, which you will also need to prepare for the FE exam. The *Review Manual* is Professional Publications' most popular study guide for both the morning and afternoon general exams. It and the *Engineer-In-Training Reference Manual* have been the most popular review books for this exam for almost 20 years.

You cannot prepare adequately without your own copy of the NCEES' *Fundamentals of Engineering (FE) Discipline Specific Reference Handbook*. This document contains the data and formulas that you will need to solve both the general and the discipline-specific problems. A good way to become familiar with it is to look up the information, formulas, and data that you need while trying to work practice problems.

No exam-prep book is ever complete. By necessity, it will change as the exam changes. Even when the exam format doesn't change for a while, new problems and improved explanations can always be added. A new edition of this book was already on the design-board as this book was going to the printer.

Michael Lindeburg
Belmont, CA

How to Use this Book

HOW EXAMINEES CAN USE THIS BOOK

This book is divided into two parts: The first part consists of 60 representative practice problems covering all of the topics in the afternoon DS exam. 60 problems happen to correspond to the number of problems in the afternoon DS exam. You may time yourself by allowing approximately 4 minutes per problem when attempting to solve these problems, but that was not my intent when designing this book. Since the solution follows directly after each problem in this section, I intended for you to read through the problems, attempt to solve them on your own, become familiar with the support material in the official NCEES *Fundamentals of Engineering (FE) Discipline Specific Reference Handbook*, and accumulate the reference materials you think you will need for additional study.

The second part of this book consists of a complete sample examination that you can use as a source of additional practice problems or as a timed diagnostic tool. It also contains 60 problems, and the number of problems in each subject corresponds to the breakdown of subjects published by NCEES. Since the solutions to this part of the book are consolidated at the end, it was my intent that you would solve these problems in a realistic mock-exam mode.

You should use the NCEES *Fundamentals of Engineering (FE) Discipline Specific Reference Handbook* as your only reference during this mock exam.

The morning general exam and the afternoon DS exam essentially cover two different bodies of knowledge. It takes a lot of discipline to prepare for two standardized exams simultaneously. Because of that (and because of my good understanding of human nature), I suspect that you will be tempted to start preparing for your chosen DS exam only after you have become comfortable with the general subjects. That's actually quite logical, because if you run out of time, you will still have the general afternoon exam as a viable option.

If, however, you are limited in time to only two or three months of study, it will be quite difficult to do a thorough DS review if you wait until after you have finished your general review. With a limited amount of time, you really need to prepare for both exams in parallel.

HOW INSTRUCTORS CAN USE THIS BOOK

The availability of the discipline-specific FE exam has greatly complicated the lives of review course instructors and coordinators. The general consensus is that it is essentially impossible to do justice to all of the general FE exam topics and then present a credible review for each of the five DS topics. Increases in course cost, expenses, course length, and instructor pools (among many other issues) all conspire to create quite a difficult situation.

One-day reviews for each DS subject are subject-overload from a reviewing examinee's standpoint. Efforts to shuffle FE students over the parallel PE review courses meet with scheduling conflicts. Another idea, that of lengthening lectures and providing more in-depth coverage of existing topics (e.g., covering transistors during the electricity lecture), is perceived as a misuse of time by a majority of the review course attendees. Is it any wonder that virtually every FE review course in the country has elected to only present reviews for the general afternoon exam?

But, while more than half of the examinees elect to take the general afternoon exam, some may actually be required to take a DS exam. This is particularly the case in some university environments where the FE exam has become useful as an "outcome assessment tool." Thus, some method of review is still needed.

Since most examinees begin reviewing approximately two to three months before the exam (which corresponds to when most review courses begin), it is impractical to wait until the end of the general review to start the DS review. The DS review must proceed in parallel with the general review.

In the absence of parallel DS lectures (something that isn't yet occurring in too many review courses), you may want to structure your review course to provide lectures only on the general subjects. Your DS review could be assigned as "independent study," using chapters and problems from this book. Thus, your DS review would consist of distributing this book with a schedule of assignments. Your instructional staff could still provide assistance on specific DS problems, and completed DS assignments could still be recorded.

The final chapter on incorporating DS subjects into review courses has yet to be written. Like the landscape architect who waits until a well-worn path appears through the plants before placing stepping stones, we need to see how review courses do it before we can give any advice.

Common Questions About the DS Exam

Q: Do I have to take the DS exam?

A: Most people do not have to take the DS exam and may elect the general exam option. The state boards do not care which afternoon option you choose; nor do employers. In some cases, examinees who are still in their undergraduate degree program may be required by their university to take a specific DS exam.

Q: Do all mechanical, civil, electrical, chemical, and industrial engineers take the DS exam?

A: Originally, the concept was that examinees from these "big five" disciplines would take the DS exam, and the general exam would be for everyone else. This remains just a concept, however. A majority of engineers in all of the disciplines apparently take the general exam.

Q: When do I elect to take the DS exam?

A: You will make your decision on the afternoon of the FE exam, when the exam booklet (containing all of the DS exams) is distributed to you.

Q: Where on the application for the FE exam do I choose which DS exam I want to take?

A: You don't specify the DS option at the time of your application.

Q: After starting to work on either the DS or general exam, can I change my mind and switch options?

A: Yes. Theoretically, if you haven't spent too much time on one exam, you can change your mind and start a different one. (You might need to obtain a new answer sheet from the proctor.)

Q: After I take the DS exam, does anyone know that I took it?

A: After you take the FE exam, only NCEES and your state board will know whether you took the DS or general exam. Such information may or may not be retained by your state board.

Q: Will my DS EIT certificate be recognized by other states?

A: Yes. All states recognize passing the FE exam and do not distinguish between the DS and general afternoon portions of the FE exam.

Q: Is the DS EIT certificate "better" than the general EIT certificate?

A: There is no difference. No one will know which option you chose. It's not stated on the certificate you receive from your state.

Q: What is the format of the DS exam?

A: The DS exam is 4 hours long. There are 60 problems, each worth 2 points. The average time per problem is 4 minutes. Each problem is multiple choice with 4 answer choices. Most problems require the application of more than one concept (i.e., formula).

Q: Is there anything special about the way the DS exam is administered?

A: In all ways, the DS and general afternoon exam are equivalent. There is no penalty for guessing. No credit is given for scratch pad work, methods, etc.

Q: Are the answer choices close or tricky?

A: Answer choices are not particularly close together in value, so the number of significant digits is not going to be an issue. Wrong answers, referred to as "distractors" by NCEES, are credible. However, the exam is not "tricky;" it does not try to mislead you.

Q: Are any problems in the afternoon related to each other?

A: Several questions may refer to the same situation or figure. However, NCEES has tried to make all of the questions independent. If you make a mistake on one question, it shouldn't carry over to another.

Q: Is there any minimum passing score for the DS exam?

A: No. It is the total score from your morning and afternoon sessions that determines your passing, not the individual session scores. You do not have to "pass" each session individually.

Q: Is the general portion easier, harder, or the same as the DS exams?

A: Theoretically, all of the afternoon options are the same. At least, that is the intent of offering the specific options: to reduce the variability. Individual passing rates, however, may still vary 5 to 10 percent from exam to exam. (Professional Publications lists the most recent passing statistics for the various DS options on its Internet web page at www.ppi2pass.com.)

Q: Do the DS exams cover material at the undergraduate or graduate level?

A: Like the general exam, test topics come entirely from the typical undergraduate degree program. However, the emphasis is primarily on material from the third and fourth year of your program. This may put examinees who take the exam in their junior year at a disadvantage.

Q: Do you need practical work experience to take the DS exam?

A: No.

Q: Does the DS exam also draw on subjects that are in the general exam?

A: Yes. The dividing line between general and DS topics is often indistinct.

Q: Is the DS exam in English or SI units?

A: The DS exam is essentially entirely in SI units. A few exceptions exist for some civil engineering subjects (surveying, hydrology, code-based design, etc.) where current common practice is limited to English units.

Q: Does the NCEES' *Fundamentals of Engineering (FE) Discipline Specific Reference Handbook* cover everything that is on the DS exam?

A: No. You may be tested on subjects that are not present in the NCEES Handbook. However, NCEES has apparently adopted an unofficial policy of providing any necessary information, data, and formulas in the stem of the question. You will not be required to memorize any formulas.

Q: When will I get my copy of the NCEES' *Fundamentals of Engineering (FE) Discipline Specific Reference Handbook*?

A: The timing of when you receive this booklet is up to your individual state, and the policies of the state are not consistent. (You can obtain a copy at any time from Professional Publications.)

Q: How is the DS reference material identified in the NCEES' *Fundamentals of Engineering (FE) Discipline Specific Reference Handbook*?

A: In most cases, the DS reference material is consolidated in the back. However, this policy is not consistently followed. In some cases, the DS reference material is mixed in with the general reference material. Only in some cases is this "intermixed" material identified as being DS material.

Q: Is everything in the DS portion of the NCEES' *Fundamentals of Engineering (FE) Discipline Specific Reference Handbook* going to be on the exam?

A: Apparently, there is a fair amount of reference material that isn't needed for every exam. There is no way, however, to know what material is needed.

Q: How long does it take to prepare for the DS exam?

A: Preparing for the DS exam is similar to preparing for a mini PE exam. Engineers typically take two to three months to complete a thorough review for the PE exam. However, examinees who are still in their degree program at a university probably aren't going to spend more than two weeks thinking about, worrying about, or preparing for the DS exam. They rely on their recent familiarity with the subject matter.

Q: If I take the DS exam and fail, do I have to take the DS exam the next time?

A: No. The examination process has no memory.

Q: Where can I get even more information about the DS exam?

A: If you have internet access, visit the Licensing Exam Forum at Professional Publications' web site. Our address is www.ppi2pass.com.

Engineering Registration in the United States

ENGINEERING REGISTRATION

Engineering registration (also known as *engineering licensing*) in the United States is an examination process by which a state's board of engineering licensing (i.e., registration board) determines and certifies that you have achieved a minimum level of competence. This process protects the public by preventing unqualified individuals from offering engineering services.

Most engineers do not need to be registered. In particular, most engineers who work for companies that design and manufacture products are exempt from the licensing requirement. This is known as the *industrial exemption*. Nevertheless, there are many good reasons for registering. For example, you cannot offer consulting engineering design services in any state unless you are registered in that state. Even within a product-oriented corporation, however, you may find that employment, advancement, or managerial positions are limited to registered engineers.

Once you have met the registration requirements, you will be allowed to use the titles Professional Engineer (PE), Registered Engineer (RE), and Consulting Engineer (CE).

Although the registration process is similar in all 50 states, each state has its own registration law. Unless you offer consulting engineering services in more than one state, however, you will not need to register in other states.

The U.S. Registration Procedure

The registration procedure is similar in most states. You will take two eight-hour written examinations. The first is the *Fundamentals of Engineering Examination*, also known as the *Engineer-In-Training Examination* and the *Intern Engineer Exam*. The initials FE, EIT, and IE are also used. This examination covers basic subjects from all of the mathematics, physics, chemistry, and engineering classes you took during your first four university years.

In rare cases, you may be allowed to skip this first examination. However, the actual details of registration qualifications, experience requirements, minimum education levels, fees, oral interviews, and examination schedules vary from state to state. Contact your state's registration board for more information.

The second eight-hour examination is the *Professional Engineering Examination*. The initials PE are also used. This examination covers subjects only from your areas of specialty.

National Council of Examiners for Engineering and Surveying

The National Council of Examiners for Engineering and Surveying (NCEES) in Clemson, South Carolina, produces, distributes, and scores the national FE and PE examinations. The individual states purchase the examinations from NCEES and administer them themselves. NCEES does not distribute applications to take the examinations, administer the examinations or appeals, or notify you of the results. These tasks are all performed by the states.

Reciprocity Among States

With minor exceptions, having a license from one state will not permit you to practice engineering in another state. You must have a professional engineering license from each state in which you work. For most engineers, this is not a problem, but for some, it is. Luckily, it is not too difficult to get a license from every state you work in once you have a license from one state.

All states use the NCEES examinations. If you take and pass the FE or PE examination in one state, your certificate will be honored by all of the other states. Although there may be other special requirements imposed by a state, it will not be necessary to retake the FE and PE examinations. The issuance of an engineering license based on another state's license is known as *reciprocity* or *comity*.

The simultaneous administration of identical examinations in all states has led to the term *uniform examination*. However, each state is still free to choose its own minimum passing score and to add special questions and requirements to the examination process. Therefore, the use of a uniform examination has not, by itself, ensured reciprocity among states.

Phone Numbers of State Boards of Registration

Alabama	(334) 242-5568	Montana	(406) 444-4285
Alaska	(907) 465-2540	Nebraska	(402) 471-2407
Arizona	(602) 255-4053	Nevada	(702) 688-1231
Arkansas	(501) 324-9085	New Hampshire	(603) 271-2219
California	(916) 263-2222	New Jersey	(201) 504-6460
Colorado	(303) 894-7788	New Mexico	(505) 827-7561
Connecticut	(860) 566-3290	New York	(518) 474-3846
Delaware	(302) 577-6500	North Carolina	(919) 781-9499
District of Columbia	(202) 727-7454	North Dakota	(701) 258-0786
Florida	(904) 488-9912	Ohio	(614) 466-3650
Georgia	(404) 656-3926	Oklahoma	(405) 521-2874
Guam	(671) 646-9386	Oregon	(503) 378-4180
Hawaii	(808) 586-3000	Pennsylvania	(717) 783-7049
Idaho	(208) 334-3860	Puerto Rico	(809) 722-2122
Illinois	(217) 782-8556	Rhode Island	(401) 277-2565
Indiana	(317) 232-2980	South Carolina	(803) 737-9260
Iowa	(515) 281-5602	South Dakota	(605) 394-2510
Kansas	(913) 296-3053	Tennessee	(615) 741-3221
Kentucky	(502) 573-2680	Texas	(512) 440-7723
Louisiana	(504) 295-8522	Utah	(801) 530-6551
Maine	(207) 287-3236	Vermont	(802) 828-2363
Maryland	(410) 333-6322	Virginia	(804) 367-8512
Massachusetts	(617) 727-9957	Virgin Islands	(809) 774-3130
Michigan	(517) 335-1669	Washington	(360) 753-6966
Minnesota	(612) 296-2388	West Virginia	(304) 558-3554
Mississippi	(601) 359-6160	Wisconsin	(608) 266-1397
Missouri	(573) 751-0047	Wyoming	(307) 777-6155

THE FE EXAMINATION

Applying for the Examination

Each state charges different fees, specifies different requirements, and uses different forms to apply for the exam. Therefore, it will be necessary to request an application from the state in which you want to become registered. Generally, it is sufficient for you to phone for this application. Telephone numbers for all U.S. state boards of registration are given in the above list.

Keep a copy of your examination application and send the original application by certified mail, requesting a receipt of delivery. Keep your proof of mailing and delivery with your copy of the application.

Examination Dates

The national FE and PE examinations are administered twice a year, on the same weekends in all states.

The following table contains the dates of upcoming examination periods.

U.S. Engineering Licensing Examination Dates

year	Spring exam	Fall exam
1997	April 18–19	October 31; November 1
1998	April 24–25	October 30–31
1999	April 23–24	October 29–30
2000	April 14–15	October 27–28

FE Examination Format

The NCEES Fundamentals of Engineering examination has the following format and characteristics.

- There are two four-hour sessions separated by a one-hour lunch.

- Examination questions are distributed in a bound examination booklet. A different examination booklet is used for each of these two sessions.

- The morning session (also known as the *A.M. session*) has 120 multiple-choice questions, each with four possible answers lettered (A) through (D). Responses must be recorded with a number 2 pencil on special answer sheets. No credit is given for answers recorded in ink.

- Each problem in the morning session is worth one point. The total score possible in the morning is 120 points. Guessing is valid; no points are subtracted for incorrect answers.

- There are questions on the examination from most of the undergraduate engineering degree program subjects. Questions from the same subject are all grouped together, and the subjects are labeled. The numbers of questions for each subject in the morning session are given in the following table.

Morning FE Exam Subjects

subject	number of questions
chemistry	11
computers	7
dynamics	9
electrical circuits	12
engineering economics	5
ethics	5
fluid mechanics	8
materials science and structure of matter	8
mathematics	24
mechanics of materials	8
statics	12
thermodynamics	11

- There are six different versions of the afternoon session (also known as the *P.M. session*), five of which correspond to a specific engineering discipline: chemical, civil, electrical, industrial, and mechanical engineering.

Each version of the afternoon session consists of 60 questions. All questions are mandatory. Questions in each subject may be grouped into related problem sets containing between two and ten questions each.

The sixth version of the afternoon examination is a general examination suitable for anyone, but in particular, for engineers whose specialties are not one of the other five disciplines. Though the subjects in the general afternoon examination correspond to the morning subjects, the questions are more complex—hence their double weighting.

Questions on the afternoon examination are intended to cover concepts learned in the last two years of a four-year degree program. Unlike morning questions, these questions may deal with more than one basic concept per question.

The numbers of questions for each subject in the general afternoon session examination are given in the following table.

Afternoon FE Exam Subjects (General Exam)

subject	number of questions
chemistry	5
computers	3
dynamics	5
electrical circuits	6
engineering economics	3
ethics	3
fluid mechanics	4
materials science and structure of matter	3
mathematics	12
mechanics of materials	4
statics	6
thermodynamics	6

The numbers of questions for each subject in the discipline-specific afternoon session examination are listed at the end of this section. The discipline-specific afternoon examinations cover substantially different bodies of knowledge than the morning examination. Formulas and tables of data needed to solve questions in these examinations will be included in either the *NCEES FE Reference Handbook* or in the body of the question statement itself.

Each afternoon question consists of a problem statement followed by multiple-choice questions. Four answer choices lettered (A) through (D) are given, from which you must choose the best answer.

- Each question in the afternoon is worth two points, making the total possible score 120 points.

- The scores from the morning and afternoon sessions are added together to determine your total score. No points are subtracted for guessing or incorrect answers. Both sessions are given equal weight. It is not necessary to achieve any minimum score on either the morning or afternoon sessions.

- All grading is done by computer optical sensing.

Use of SI Units on the FE Exam

Starting with the October 1995 examination, approximately 65 percent of the numerical questions (i.e., those requiring calculations) used metric units. Metric questions appear in all subjects, except some civil engineering and surveying subjects that typically use only U.S. customary (i.e., English) units. Some of the remaining questions may be presented on the exam in both metric and English units. These questions are actually stated twice, once in metric units and once in English units. Dual dimensioning is not used. However, these dual-statement questions are rapidly being phased out.

NCEES intends the FE examination to be 100 percent metric on or before October 2008. However, NCEES is already approximately seven years ahead of the metrification schedule mandated by its board of directors.

It is the goal of NCEES to use SI units that are consistent with ANSI/IEEE standard 268-1992 (the American Standard for Metric Practice). Non-SI metric units might still be used when common or where needed for consistency with tabulated data (e.g., use of bars in pressure measurement).

Grading and Scoring the FE Exam

The FE exam is not graded on the curve, and there is no guarantee that a certain percent of examinees will pass. Rather, NCEES uses a modification of the Angoff procedure to determine the suggested passing score (the cutoff point or cut score).

With this method, a group of engineering professors and other experts estimate the fraction of minimally qualified engineers that will be able to answer each question correctly. The summation of the estimated fractions for all test questions becomes the passing score. The passing score in recent years has been somewhat less than 50 percent (i.e., a raw score of approximately 110 points out of 240). Because the law in most states requires engineers to achieve a score of 70 percent to become licensed, you may be reported as having achieved a score of 70 percent if your raw score is greater than the passing score established by NCEES, regardless of the raw percentage. The actual score may be slightly more or slightly less than 110 as determined from the performance of all examinees on the equating subtest.

Approximately 20 percent of each FE exam consists of questions repeated from previous examinations—this is the *equating subtest*. Since the performance of previous examinees on the equating subtest is known, comparisons can be made between the two examinations and examinee populations. These comparisons are used to adjust the passing score.

The individual states are free to adopt their own passing score, but all adopt NCEES' suggested passing score because the states believe this cutoff score can be defended if challenged.

You will receive the results approximately 12 to 14 weeks after the examination. If you pass, your score may or may not be revealed to you, depending on your state's policy, but if you fail, you will receive your score.

The following table lists the approximate fractions of examinees passing the FE exam.

Approximate FE Exam Passing Rates

category	percent passing
total, all U.S. states	60%–70%
ABET accredited, four-year engineering degrees[a]	70%–80%
nonaccredited, four-year engineering degrees	50%–65%
ABET accredited, four-year technology degrees[a]	35%–45%
nonaccredited, four-year technology degrees	25%–35%
nongraduates	35%–40%

[a] The Accreditation Board for Engineering and Technology (ABET) reviews and approves engineering degree programs in the United States. No engineering degree programs offered by universities outside of the United States and its territories or the Commonwealth of Puerto Rico are accredited by ABET.

Permitted Reference Material

Since October 1993, the FE examination has been what NCEES calls a "limited-reference" exam. This means that no books or references other than those supplied by NCEES may be used. Therefore, the FE examination is really an "NCEES-publication only" exam. NCEES provides its own *FE Reference Handbook* for use during the examination. No books from other publishers may be used.

CALCULATORS

In most states, any battery- or solar-powered, silent calculator can be used, although printers cannot be used. (The solar-powered calculators are preferred because they do not have batteries that run down.) In most states, there are no restrictions on programmable, preprogrammed, or business/finance calculators. Similarly, nomographs and specialty slide rules are permitted. To prevent unauthorized transcription and redistribution of the examination questions, calculators with significant word processing functions have been banned by some states. You cannot share calculators with other examinees.

It is essential that a calculator used for engineering examinations have the following functions.

- trigonometric functions
- inverse trigonometric functions
- hyperbolic functions
- pi
- square root and x^2
- common and natural logarithms
- y^x and e^x

For maximum speed, your calculator should also have or be programmed for the following functions.

- extracting roots of quadratic and higher-order equations
- converting between polar (phasor) and rectangular vectors
- finding standard deviations and variances
- calculating determinants of 3×3 matrices
- linear regression
- economic analysis and other financial functions

STRATEGIES FOR PASSING THE FE EXAM

The most successful strategy to pass the FE exam is to prepare in all of the examination subjects. Do not limit the number of subjects you study in hopes of finding enough questions in your particular areas of knowledge to pass.

Fast recall and stamina are essential to doing well. You must be able to quickly recall solution procedures, formulas, and important data. You will not have time during the exam to derive solutions methods—you must know them instinctively. This ability must be maintained for eight hours. Be sure to gain familiarity with the *NCEES FE Reference Handbook* by using it as your only reference for some of the problems you work when you study.

In order to get exposure to all examination subjects, it is imperative that you develop and adhere to a review schedule. If you are not taking a classroom review course (where the order of your preparation is determined by the lectures), prepare your own review schedule.

There are also physical demands on your body during the examination. It is very difficult to remain alert and attentive for eight hours or more. Unfortunately, the more time you study, the less time you have to maintain your physical condition. Thus, most examinees arrive at the examination site in peak mental condition but in deteriorated physical condition. While preparing for the FE exam is not the only good reason for embarking on a physical conditioning program, it can serve as a good incentive to get in shape.

It will be helpful to make a few simple decisions prior to starting your review. You should be aware of the different options available to you. For example, you should decide early on to

- use SI units in your preparation
- perform electrical calculations with effective (rms) or maximum values
- take calculations out to a maximum of four significant digits
- prepare in all examination subjects, not just your specialty areas

At the beginning of your review program, you should locate a spare calculator. It is not necessary to buy a spare if you can arrange to borrow one from a friend or the office. However, if possible, your primary and spare calculators should be identical. If your spare calculator is not identical to the primary calculator, spend a few minutes familiarizing yourself with its functions.

A Few Days Before the Exam

There are a few things you should do a week or so before the examination date. For example, visit the exam site in order to find the building, parking areas, examination room, and rest rooms. You should also make arrangements for child care and transportation. Since the examination does not always start or end at the designated times, make sure that your child care and transportation arrangements can tolerate a later-than-scheduled completion.

Second in importance to your scholastic preparation is the preparation of your two examination kits. The first kit consists of a bag or box containing items to bring with you into the examination room.

[ ]   letter admitting you to the examination
[ ]   photographic identification
[ ]   main calculator
[ ]   spare calculator
[ ]   extra calculator batteries
[ ]   supply of number 2 pencils
[ ]   mechanical pencil and extra leads
[ ]   a large eraser
[ ]   unobtrusive snacks
[ ]   travel pack of tissues
[ ]   headache remedy
[ ] $2.00 in change

[ ]   light, comfortable sweater
[ ]   loose shoes or slippers
[ ]   handkerchief
[ ]   cushion for your chair
[ ]   small hand towel
[ ]   earplugs
[ ]   wristwatch with alarm
[ ]   wire coat hanger
[ ]   extra set of car keys

The second kit consists of the following items and should be left in a separate bag or box in your car in case they are needed.

[ ]   copy of your application
[ ]   proof of delivery
[ ]   this book
[ ]   other references
[ ]   regular dictionary
[ ]   scientific dictionary
[ ]   course notes in three-ring binders
[ ]   cardboard box (use as a bookcase)
[ ]   instruction booklets for all your calculators
[ ]   light lunch
[ ]   beverages in thermos and cans
[ ]   sunglasses
[ ]   extra pair of prescription glasses
[ ]   raincoat, boots, gloves, hat, and umbrella
[ ]   street map of the examination site
[ ]   note to the parking patrol for your windshield explaining where you are, what you are doing, and why your time may have expired.
[ ]   battery-powered desk lamp

The Day Before the Exam

Take the day before the examination off from work to relax. Do not cram the last night. A good prior night's sleep is the best way to start the examination. If you live far from the examination site, consider getting a hotel room in which to spend the night.

Make sure your exam kits are packed and ready to go.

The Day of the Exam

You should arrive at least 30 minutes before the examination starts. This will allow time for finding a convenient parking place, bringing your materials to the examination room, and making room and seating changes. Be prepared, though, to find that the examination room is not open or ready at the designated time.

Once the examination has started, consider the following suggestions.

- Set your wristwatch alarm for five minutes before the end of each four-hour session and use that remaining time to guess at all of the remaining unsolved problems. Do not work up until the very end. You will be successful with about 25 percent of your guesses, and these points will more than make up for the few points you might earn by working during the last five minutes.

- Do not spend more than two minutes per morning question. (The average time available per problem is two minutes.) If you have not finished a question in that time, make a note of it and continue on.

- Do not ask your proctors technical questions. Even if they are knowledgeable in engineering, they will not be permitted to answer your questions.

- Make a quick mental note about any problems for which you cannot find a correct response or for which you believe there are two correct answers. Errors in the exam are rare, but they do occur. Being able to point out an error later might give you the margin you need to pass. Since such problems are almost always discovered during the scoring process and discounted from the examination, it is not necessary to tell your proctor, but be sure to mark the one best answer before moving on.

- Make sure all of your responses on the answer sheet are dark and completely fill the bubbles.

The following tables list the new FE afternoon discipline-specific exam subjects with their corresponding categories and numbers of each type of question as released by NCEES.

Afternoon FE Exam Subjects (Discipline-Specific Exams)

CHEMICAL ENGINEERING

subject	number of questions
chemical reaction engineering	6
chemical thermodynamics	6
computer and numerical methods	3
heat transfer	6
mass transfer	6
material/energy balances	9
pollution prevention (waste minimization)	3
process control	3
process design and economics evaluation	6
process equipment design	3
process safety	3
transport phenomena	6

CIVIL ENGINEERING

subject	number of questions
computers and numerical methods	6
construction management	3
environmental engineering	6
hydraulics and hydrologic systems	6
legal and professional aspects	3
soil mechanics and foundations	6
structural analysis (frames, trusses, etc.)	6
structural design (concrete, steel, etc.)	6
surveying	6
transportation facilities	6
water purification and treatment	6

ELECTRICAL ENGINEERING

subject	number of questions
analog electronic circuits	6
communications theory	6
computer and numerical methods	3
computer hardware engineering	3
computer software engineering	3
control systems theory and analysis	6
digital systems	6
electromagnetic theory and applications	6
instrumentation	3
network analysis	6
power systems	3
signal processing	3
solid state electronics and devices	6

INDUSTRIAL ENGINEERING

subject	number of questions
computer computations and modeling	3
design of industrial experiments	3
engineering economics	3
engineering statistics	3
facility design and location	3
industrial cost analysis	3
industrial ergonomics	3
industrial management	3
information system design	3
manufacturing processes	3
manufacturing systems design	3
material handling system design	3
mathematical optimization and modeling	3
production planning and scheduling	3
productivity measurement and management	3
queuing theory and modeling	3
simulation	3
statistical quality control	3
total quality management	3
work performance and methods	3

MECHANICAL ENGINEERING

subject	number of questions
automatic controls	3
computer (numerical methods, automation, etc.)	3
dynamic systems (vibrations, kinematics, etc.)	6
energy conversion and power plants	3
fans, pumps, and compressors	3
fluid mechanics	6
heat transfer	6
material behavior/processing	3
measurement and instrumentation	6
mechanical design	6
refrigeration and HVAC	3
stress analysis	6
thermodynamics	6

The National Society of Professional Engineers

Whether you design water works, consumer goods, or aerospace vehicles; whether you work in private industry, for the U.S. government, or for the public; and whether your efforts are theoretical or practical, you (as an engineer) have a significant responsibility.

Engineers of all types perform exciting and rewarding work, often stretching new technologies to their limits. But those limits are often incomprehensible to nonengineers. As the ambient level of technical sophistication increases, the public has come to depend increasingly and unhesitatingly more on engineers. That is where professional licensing and the National Society of Professional Engineers (NSPE) become important.

NSPE, the leading organization for licensed engineering professionals, is dedicated to serving the engineering profession by supporting activities, such as continuing educational programs for its members, lobbying and legislative efforts on local and national levels, and the promotion of guidelines for ethical service. From local, community-based projects to encourage top-scoring high school students to choose engineering as a career, to hard-hitting lobbying efforts in the nation's capital to satisfy the needs of all engineers, NSPE is committed to you and your profession.

Engineering licensing is a two-way street: it benefits you while it benefits the public and the profession. For you, licensing offers a variety of benefits, ranging from peer recognition to greater advancement and career opportunities. For the profession, licensing establishes a common credential by which all engineers can be compared. For the public, a professional engineering license is an assurance of a recognizable standard of competence.

NSPE has always been a strong advocate of engineering licensing and a supporter of the profession. Professional Publications hopes you will consider membership in NSPE as the next logical step in your career advancement. For more information regarding membership, write to the National Society of Professional Engineers, Information Center, 1420 King Street, Alexandria, VA 22314, or call (703) 684-2800.

Practice Problems

AUTOMATIC CONTROLS

1. What is the reduced canonical form of the following block diagram?

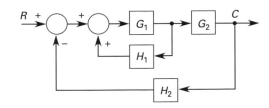

(A)

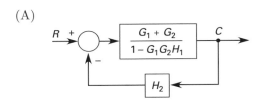

(B)

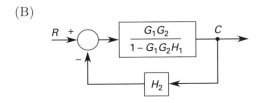

(C)

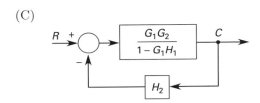

(D)

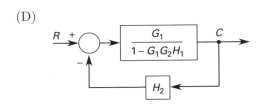

Solution:

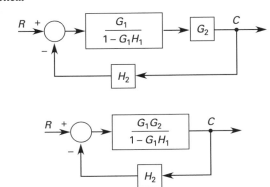

Answer is C.

2. Consider a system whose input and output are related by the following differential equation.

$$\frac{d^2y}{dt^2} + 5\frac{dy}{dt} - 10y = 2x - \frac{dx}{dt}$$

Assuming that the initial conditions are all zero, what is the transfer function of the system?

(A) $\dfrac{2 + s}{s^2 - 25s + 100}$

(B) $\dfrac{s}{s^2 - 10}$

(C) $\dfrac{2 - s}{s^2 + 5s - 10}$

(D) $\dfrac{s^2 + 5s - 10}{2 - s}$

Solution:

The Laplace transform of the differential equation is

$$s^2 y(s) + 5sy(s) - 10y(s) = 2x(s) - sx(s)$$

$$y(s) = \left(\frac{2 - s}{s^2 + 5s - 10}\right) x(s)$$

The transfer function is

$$P(s) = \frac{y(s)}{x(s)} = \frac{2 - s}{s^2 + 5s - 10}$$

Answer is C.

3. A system has the pole-zero map in the s-plane shown. What is the transfer function of the system with a gain factor of 4?

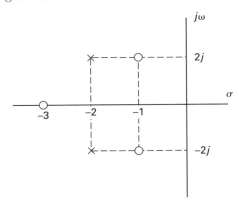

(A) $\dfrac{(4)(s + 3)(s + 1 + 2j)(s + 1 - 2j)}{(s + 2 + 2j)(s + 2 - 2j)}$

(B) $\dfrac{(4)(s + 2 + 2j)(s + 2 - 2j)}{(s + 3)(s + 1 + 2j)(s + 1 - 2j)}$

(C) $\dfrac{(s - 3)(s - 1 + 2j)(s - 1 - 2j)}{(4)(s + 2 + 2j)(s + 2 - 2j)}$

(D) $\dfrac{(s - 2 - 2j)(s - 2 + 2j)}{(4)(s + 3)(s + 1 + 2j)(s + 2 - 2j)}$

Solution:

The poles are

$$-2 + 2j$$
$$-2 - 2j$$

The zeros are

$$-1 + 2j$$
$$-1 - 2j$$
$$-3$$

$$G(s) = \frac{(4)(s+3)(s+1+2j)(s+1-2j)}{(s+2+2j)(s+2-2j)}$$

Answer is A.

COMPUTERS

4. A program is given as follows.

```
CAPITAL = 4200
RATE = 0.01
NET = CAPITAL*(RATE + 1)
IF NET < 5000 THEN NET = CAPITAL
PRINT NET
END
```

After execution, what is the printed output?

(A) 3600
(B) 4200
(C) 4600
(D) 5000

Solution:

$$NET = (4200)(1.01) = 4242 < 5000$$
$$= 4200$$

Answer is B.

5. The following program segment references a function statement as shown.

```
DEFN F(Z) = 3*LOG₁₀(Z) + SQRT(Z)
Z = 2.5
X = F(Z)*10
PRINT X
END
```

After execution, what is the printed output?

(A) 17
(B) 28
(C) 36
(D) 63

Solution:

$$F(Z) = 3\log_{10}(Z) + \sqrt{Z}$$
$$X = \left(3\log_{10}(2.5) + \sqrt{2.5}\right)(10)$$
$$= 27.75 \quad (28)$$

Answer is B.

6. A program segment contains a loop as shown.

```
START = 2
END = 4
FACT = 1
LOOP(INDEX = START TO END,INCR = 1)
    FACT = FACT*INDEX
END LOOP
```

What is the final value of FACT at the end of the loop?

(A) 8
(B) 16
(C) 24
(D) 32

Solution:

The loop counter begins at 2 and goes to 4 in increments of 1.

```
FACT = 1
INDEX = 2
FACT = 1 × 2
INDEX = 3
FACT = 1 × 2 × 3
INDEX = 4
FACT = 1 × 2 × 3 × 4 = 24
END
```

Answer is C.

DYNAMIC SYSTEMS

7. A 10 g ball is released vertically from a height of 10 m. The ball strikes a horizontal surface and bounces back. The coefficient of restitution between the surface and the ball is 0.75. The height that the ball will reach after bouncing is most nearly

(A) 3.5 m
(B) 5.6 m
(C) 8.5 m
(D) 11 m

Solution:

The velocity of the ball just prior to impact can be found from the conservation of energy principle.

$$KE = PE$$
$$\tfrac{1}{2}mv_o^2 = mgh_o$$
$$v_o = \sqrt{2gh_o}$$

The velocity of the ball just after impact is found from

$$e = \frac{v_r}{v_o} = \frac{v_r}{\sqrt{2gh_o}}$$

Use the conservation of energy principle to find the rebound height.

$$\tfrac{1}{2}mv_r^2 = mgh_r$$
$$h_r = \frac{v_r^2}{2g} = e^2 h_o$$
$$= (0.75)^2(10 \text{ m})$$
$$= 5.625 \text{ m} \quad (5.6 \text{ m})$$

Answer is B.

8. A 5 g mass is to be placed on a 50 cm diameter horizontal table that is rotating at 50 rev/min. It is required that the mass not slide away from its position. The coefficient of friction between the mass and the table is 0.2. What is the maximum distance that the mass can be placed from the axis of rotation?

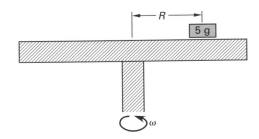

(A) 2 cm
(B) 7 cm
(C) 12 cm
(D) 25 cm

Solution:

Balance the centrifugal (radial) and frictional forces.

$$\sum F = 0$$
$$F_c - F_f = 0 \qquad \textit{Eq. 1}$$
$$F_c = ma_r = m\omega^2 R \qquad \textit{Eq. 2}$$
$$F_f = \mu N = \mu W = \mu mg \qquad \textit{Eq. 3}$$

Substitute Eq. 2 and Eq. 3 into Eq. 1 and solve for R.

$$R = \frac{\mu g}{\omega^2} = \frac{(0.2)\left(9.81\,\frac{\text{m}}{\text{s}^2}\right)}{\left(\left(50\,\frac{\text{rev}}{\text{min}}\right)\left(\frac{1}{60}\,\frac{\text{min}}{\text{s}}\right)\left(2\pi\,\frac{\text{rad}}{\text{rev}}\right)\right)^2}$$
$$= 0.0716 \text{ m} \quad (7 \text{ cm})$$

Answer is B.

9. A truck of 4000 kg mass is traveling on a horizontal road at a speed of 95 km/h. At an instant of time its brakes are applied, locking the wheels. The dynamic coefficient of friction between the wheels and the road is 0.42. The stopping distance of the truck is most nearly

(A) 55 m
(B) 70 m
(C) 85 m
(D) 100 m

Solution:

$$\sum F = ma$$
$$-F_f = m\frac{dv}{dt} \qquad \textit{Eq. 1}$$
$$F_f = \mu N = \mu mg \qquad \textit{Eq. 2}$$
$$\frac{dv}{dt} = \frac{dv}{dx}\frac{dx}{dt} = v\frac{dv}{dx} \qquad \textit{Eq. 3}$$

Substituting Eq. 2 and Eq. 3 into Eq. 1,

$$-\mu mg = mv\frac{dv}{dx}$$
$$-\mu g\,dx = v\,dv \qquad \textit{Eq. 4}$$

Integrating Eq. 4,

$$-\mu g(x_2 - x_1) = \left(\tfrac{1}{2}\right)(v_2^2 - v_1^2)$$

$$x_2 = x_1 - \frac{v_2^2 - v_1^2}{2\mu g}$$

$$= 0 - \frac{0 - \left(\left(95\,\frac{\text{km}}{\text{h}}\right)\left(1000\,\frac{\text{m}}{\text{km}}\right)\left(\frac{1}{3600}\,\frac{\text{h}}{\text{s}}\right)\right)^2}{(2)(0.42)\left(9.81\,\frac{\text{m}}{\text{s}^2}\right)}$$

$$= 84.5 \text{ m} \quad (85 \text{ m})$$

Answer is C.

10.   A translating and rotating ring of mass 1 kg, angular speed of 500 rpm, and translational speed of 1 m/s is placed on a horizontal surface. The coefficient of friction between the ring and the surface is 0.35.

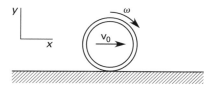

For an outside radius of 3 cm, the time at which skidding stops and rolling begins is most nearly

    (A)   0.01 s
    (B)   0.1 s
    (C)   1 s
    (D)   10 s

Solution:

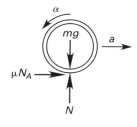

$$\sum F_x = ma$$
$$\mu N_A = ma \qquad \text{Eq. 1}$$
$$\sum F_y = 0$$
$$N = mg \qquad \text{Eq. 2}$$
$$\sum M = I\alpha$$
$$\mu NR = 3mR^2\alpha \qquad \text{Eq. 3}$$

From Eqs. 1 and 2, $a = \mu g$. From Eq. 3, $\alpha = \mu g/3R$.

$$v = v_0 + \mu g t \qquad \text{Eq. 4}$$
$$\alpha = \frac{d\omega}{dt}$$
$$\omega = \omega_0 - \left(\frac{\mu g}{3R}\right)t \qquad \text{Eq. 5}$$

When skidding stops, $v = R\omega$. Multiply Eq. 5 by R and compare with Eq. 4.

$$t = \frac{R\omega_0 - v_0}{\mu g\left(1 + \dfrac{1}{3}\right)}$$

$$= \frac{(0.03\text{ m})\left(\left(500\,\dfrac{\text{rev}}{\text{min}}\right)\left(2\pi\,\dfrac{\text{rad}}{\text{rev}}\right)\left(\dfrac{1}{60}\,\dfrac{\text{min}}{\text{s}}\right)\right) - 1\,\dfrac{\text{m}}{\text{s}}}{(0.35)\left(9.81\,\dfrac{\text{m}}{\text{s}^2}\right)\left(\dfrac{4}{3}\right)}$$

$$= 0.125\text{ s}\quad(0.1\text{ s})$$

Answer is B.

11.   A stationary uniform rod of length 1 m is struck at its tip by a 3 kg rigid ball moving horizontally with velocity of 8 m/s as shown. The mass of the rod is 7 kg, and the coefficient of restitution between the rod and the ball is 0.75.

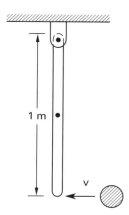

The velocity of the ball after impact is most nearly

    (A)   2.0 m/s
    (B)   3.5 m/s
    (C)   6.0 m/s
    (D)   10.5 m/s

Solution:

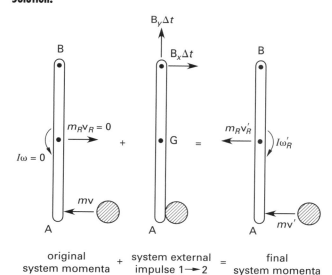

original system momenta + system external impulse 1→2 = final system momenta

Let the subscript R represent the rod.

$$\sum M_B:$$
$$mv(1.0\text{ m}) = mv'(1.0\text{ m}) + m_R v'_R(0.5\text{ m})$$
$$+ I\omega'_R \qquad \text{Eq. 1}$$
$$v'_R = R\omega'_R = (0.5\text{ m})\omega'_R$$

$$I = \tfrac{1}{12}mL^2$$
$$= \left(\frac{1}{12}\right)(7 \text{ kg})(1.0 \text{ m})^2$$
$$= 0.583 \text{ kg·m}^2$$

Substitute values into Eq. 1.

$$24 \ \frac{\text{kg·m}^2}{\text{s}} = (3 \text{ kg·m})v' + (2.33 \text{ kg·m}^2)\omega'_R \quad \textit{Eq. 2}$$
$$v'_A - v' = e(v - v_A)$$
$$= (0.75)\left(8 \ \frac{\text{m}}{\text{s}} - 0\right)$$
$$= 6 \text{ m/s} \qquad\qquad \textit{Eq. 3}$$
$$v'_A = R\omega' = (1.0 \text{ m})\omega'_R \qquad \textit{Eq. 4}$$

Solving Eqs. 2, 3, and 4 simultaneously,

$$v' = 1.88 \text{ m/s}$$

Answer is A.

ENERGY CONVERSION AND POWER PLANTS

12.   The enthalpy values at key points of an ideal reheat steam cycle are shown.

state	h, kJ/kg
1	3138.3
2	2554.1
3	3271.9
4	2470.9
5	191.83
6	199.9

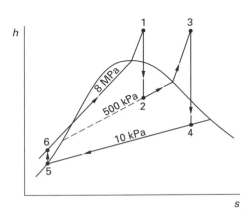

The thermal efficiency of the cycle is most nearly

(A)   33%
(B)   38%
(C)   40%
(D)   42%

Solution:

$$\eta_{\text{th}} = \frac{W_{\text{net out}}}{Q_{\text{input}}} = \frac{(h_1 - h_2) + (h_3 - h_4) - (h_6 - h_5)}{(h_1 - h_6) + (h_3 - h_2)}$$

$$= \frac{\begin{pmatrix}3138.3 \ \dfrac{\text{kJ}}{\text{kg}} - 2554.1 \ \dfrac{\text{kJ}}{\text{kg}}\end{pmatrix} + \begin{pmatrix}3271.9 \ \dfrac{\text{kJ}}{\text{kg}} - 2470.9 \ \dfrac{\text{kJ}}{\text{kg}}\end{pmatrix} - \begin{pmatrix}199.9 \ \dfrac{\text{kJ}}{\text{kg}} - 191.83 \ \dfrac{\text{kJ}}{\text{kg}}\end{pmatrix}}{\begin{pmatrix}3138.3 \ \dfrac{\text{kJ}}{\text{kg}} - 199.9 \ \dfrac{\text{kJ}}{\text{kg}}\end{pmatrix} + \begin{pmatrix}3271.9 \ \dfrac{\text{kJ}}{\text{kg}} - 2554.1 \ \dfrac{\text{kJ}}{\text{kg}}\end{pmatrix}}$$

$$= 37.67\% \quad (38\%)$$

Answer is B.

13.   An air-standard Otto cycle has a compression ratio of 8.0. At the beginning of the compression stroke the temperature is 300K and the pressure is 100 kPa. The maximum temperature in the cycle is 1000K. Assuming constant specific heats, the mean effective pressure of the cycle is most nearly

(A)   140 kPa
(B)   170 kPa
(C)   200 kPa
(D)   220 kPa

Solution:

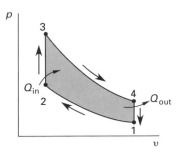

$$v_1 = \frac{RT_1}{p_1} = \frac{\left(0.287 \ \dfrac{\text{kJ}}{\text{kg·K}}\right)(300\text{K})}{100 \text{ kPa}} = 0.861 \text{ m}^3/\text{kg}$$

The compression ratio is a ratio of volumes.

$$v_2 = \frac{v_1}{r_c} = \frac{0.861 \ \dfrac{\text{m}^3}{\text{kg}}}{8.0} = 0.1076 \text{ m}^3/\text{kg}$$

$$\frac{T_2}{T_1} = \left(\frac{v_1}{v_2}\right)^{k-1}$$

$$T_2 = (300\text{K})(8.0)^{1.4-1} = 689.2\text{K}$$

$$q_{2-3} + w_{2-3} = u_3 - u_2 \quad [w_{2-3} = 0]$$

$$q_{2-3} = u_3 - u_2 = c_v(T_3 - T_2)$$
$$= \left(0.7165 \; \frac{\text{kJ}}{\text{kg·K}}\right)(1000\text{K} - 689.2\text{K})$$
$$= 222.7 \; \text{kJ/kg}$$

$$\frac{T_4}{T_3} = \left(\frac{v_3}{v_4}\right)^{k-1}$$

$$T_4 = (1000\text{K})\left(\frac{1}{8.0}\right)^{1.4-4} = 435.3\text{K}$$

$$q_{4-1} = u_1 - u_4 = c_v(T_1 - T_4)$$
$$= \left(0.7165 \; \frac{\text{kJ}}{\text{kg·K}}\right)(300\text{K} - 435.3\text{K})$$
$$= -96.94 \; \text{kJ/kg}$$

The mean effective pressure is

$$\text{mep} = \frac{|w_{\text{net out}}|}{v_1 - v_2} = \frac{|q_{\text{in}} - q_{\text{out}}|}{v_1 - v_2}$$

$$= \frac{222.7 \; \frac{\text{kJ}}{\text{kg}} - 96.94 \; \frac{\text{kJ}}{\text{kg}}}{0.861 \; \frac{\text{m}^3}{\text{kg}} - 0.1076 \; \frac{\text{m}^3}{\text{kg}}}$$

$$= 166.9 \; \text{kPa} \quad (170 \; \text{kPa})$$

Answer is B.

14. The components of a gas turbine operating at steady state are shown. The air enters the compressor at 300K and 100 kPa and is compressed to 800 kPa. The compressor's isentropic efficiency is 80%.

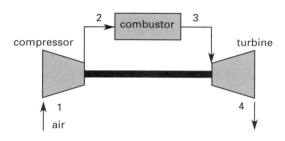

Assuming air to be an ideal gas with constant specific heats, the work required by the compressor is most nearly

    (A) 300 kJ/kg
    (B) 325 kJ/kg
    (C) 330 kJ/kg
    (D) 340 kJ/kg

Solution:

$$\frac{T_{2s}}{T_1} = \left(\frac{p_2}{p_1}\right)^{\frac{k-1}{k}}$$

$$T_{2s} = (300\text{K})\left(\frac{800 \; \text{kPa}}{100 \; \text{kPa}}\right)^{\frac{1.4-1}{1.4}} = 543.4\text{K}$$

$$\eta = \frac{W_{\text{isentropic}}}{W_{\text{actual}}} = \frac{h_{2s} - h_1}{h_2 - h_1}$$

$$W_{\text{actual}} = h_2 - h_1 = \frac{h_{2s} - h_1}{\eta} = \frac{c_p(T_{2s} - T_1)}{\eta}$$

$$= \frac{\left(1.0035 \; \frac{\text{kJ}}{\text{kg·K}}\right)(543.4\text{K} - 300\text{K})}{0.8}$$

$$= 305.3 \; \text{kJ/kg} \quad (300 \; \text{kJ/kg})$$

Answer is A.

FANS, PUMPS, AND COMPRESSORS

15. A pump is used to draw water from a lake as shown. The friction head loss in the intake line is 1.5 m of water. The pump is located at an elevation of 6 m from the surface, as indicated. The water temperature is 20°C. The vapor pressure of 20°C water is 2.339 kPa.

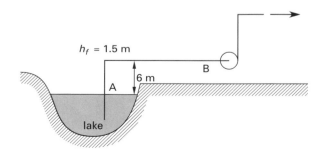

The net positive suction head available is most nearly

    (A) 2.6 m of water
    (B) 4.5 m of water
    (C) 7.5 m of water
    (D) 10.5 m of water

Solution:

The atmospheric head is

$$\frac{p_A}{\rho g} = \frac{(101.3 \; \text{kPa})\left(1000 \; \frac{\text{Pa}}{\text{kPa}}\right)}{\left(1000 \; \frac{\text{kg}}{\text{m}^3}\right)\left(9.81 \; \frac{\text{m}}{\text{s}^2}\right)} = 10.3 \; \text{m H}_2\text{O}$$

At 20°C, the vapor pressure head is

$$\frac{p_{\rm v}}{\rho g} = \frac{2.339 \times 10^3 \text{ Pa}}{\left(1000 \ \frac{\text{kg}}{\text{m}^3}\right)\left(9.81 \ \frac{\text{m}}{\text{s}^2}\right)} = 0.24 \text{ m H}_2\text{O}$$

The net positive suction head available is

$$\text{NPSHA} = \frac{p_{\rm A}}{\rho g} - z_{\rm B} - h_f - \frac{p_{\rm v}}{\rho g}$$

$$= 10.3 \text{ m} - 6 \text{ m} - 1.5 \text{ m} - 0.24 \text{ m}$$

$$= 2.56 \text{ m} \quad (2.6 \text{ m})$$

Answer is A.

16. The system characteristic for a centrifugal pump is shown. 20°C water flows through 100 m of 20 cm diameter pipe. The pipe is made of galvanized iron with a friction factor of 0.02.

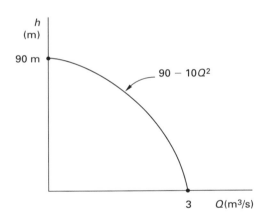

The flow rate is most nearly

(A) 0.4 m³/s
(B) 0.7 m³/s
(C) 1.0 m³/s
(D) 1.5 m³/s

Solution:

$$h_p = h_f$$

$$90 - 10Q^2 = \frac{fLv^2}{2Dg} = \frac{8fLQ^2}{\pi^2 g D^5}$$

$$= \frac{(8)(0.02)(100 \text{ m})Q^2}{\pi^2 \left(9.81 \ \frac{\text{m}}{\text{s}^2}\right)(0.2 \text{ m})^5} = 516.4Q^2$$

$$Q = \sqrt{\frac{90 \text{ m}}{10 \ \frac{\text{s}^2}{\text{m}^5} + 516.4 \ \frac{\text{s}^2}{\text{m}^5}}}$$

$$= 0.413 \text{ m}^3/\text{s} \quad (0.4 \text{ m}^2/\text{s})$$

Answer is A.

17. A ventilating fan accelerates air with a density of 1.23 kg/m³ to 20 m/s in a 0.5 m diameter duct. The power input to the fan blades is 1.5 kW.

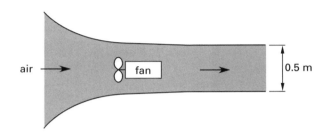

The efficiency of the fan is most nearly

(A) 40%
(B) 65%
(C) 75%
(D) 85%

Solution:

The mass flow rate is

$$\dot{m} = \rho_2 v_2 A_2 = \left(1.23 \ \frac{\text{kg}}{\text{m}^3}\right)\left(20 \ \frac{\text{m}}{\text{s}}\right)\left(\frac{\pi}{4}\right)(0.5 \text{ m})^2$$

$$= 4.83 \text{ kg/s}$$

The ideal work per unit mass is the kinetic energy.

$$W = \frac{v_2^2}{2} = \frac{\left(20 \ \frac{\text{m}}{\text{s}}\right)^2}{2} = 200 \text{ J/kg}$$

The work performed per unit mass is

$$W_{\text{actual}} = \frac{P}{\dot{m}} = \frac{(1.5 \text{ kW})\left(1000 \ \frac{\text{W}}{\text{kW}}\right)}{4.83 \ \frac{\text{kg}}{\text{s}}} = 310.6 \text{ J/kg}$$

$$\eta = \frac{W_{\text{ideal}}}{W_{\text{actual}}} = \frac{200 \ \frac{\text{J}}{\text{kg}}}{310.6 \ \frac{\text{J}}{\text{kg}}} = 0.644 \quad (65\%)$$

Answer is B.

FLUID MECHANICS

18.   A sphere, 10 cm in diameter, floats in 20°C water with half of its volume submerged. The density of water at 20°C is 998 kg/m³. The mass of the sphere is most nearly

(A) 0.2 kg
(B) 0.26 kg
(C) 0.30 kg
(D) 2.6 kg

Solution:

The buoyant force is equal to the weight of the sphere.

$$W = F_b = mg = \rho_{\text{water}} V g$$

The submerged volume is

$$V = \tfrac{1}{2}V_{\text{sphere}} = \left(\frac{1}{2}\right)\left(\frac{\pi}{6}\right)D^3$$

$$= \left(\frac{1}{2}\right)\left(\frac{\pi}{6}\right)(0.1 \text{ m})^3$$

$$= 0.2618 \times 10^{-3} \text{ m}^3$$

$$m = \rho_{\text{water}} V$$

$$= \left(998 \ \frac{\text{kg}}{\text{m}^3}\right)(0.2618 \times 10^{-3} \text{ m}^3)$$

$$= 0.261 \text{ kg} \quad (0.26 \text{ kg})$$

Answer is B.

19.   A rectangular gate 0.5 m wide is located in a fresh water tank at a slope of 45°C as shown. The gate is hinged along the top edge and is held in place by a force F at the bottom edge.

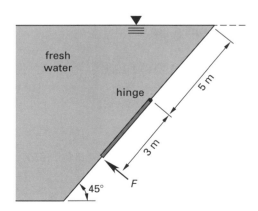

Neglecting the weight of the gate and any friction at the hinge, the force F is most nearly

(A) 21 kN
(B) 32 kN
(C) 36 kN
(D) 43 kN

Solution:

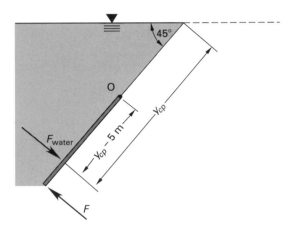

$$F_{\text{water}} = \rho g h_{cg} A$$

$$= \left(1000 \ \frac{\text{kg}}{\text{m}^3}\right)\left(9.81 \ \frac{\text{m}}{\text{s}^2}\right)(6.5 \text{ m})(\sin 45°)$$

$$\times (0.5 \text{ m})(3 \text{ m})$$

$$= 67\,633 \text{ N}$$

$$y_{cg} = 5 \text{ m} + \frac{3 \text{ m}}{2} = 6.5 \text{ m}$$

The location of this force is

$$y_{cp} = \frac{I_{cg}}{y_{cg}A} + y_{cg}$$

$$= \frac{\left(\dfrac{1}{12}\right)(0.5 \text{ m})(3 \text{ m})^3}{(6.5 \text{ m})\big((0.5 \text{ m})(3 \text{ m})\big)} + 6.5 \text{ m}$$

$$= 6.6154 \text{ m}$$

$$\sum M_{\text{hinge}} = 0$$

$$F_{\text{water}}(y_{cp} - 5 \text{ m}) = F(3 \text{ m})$$

$$F = \frac{(67\,633 \text{ N})(6.6154 \text{ m} - 5 \text{ m})}{3 \text{ m}}$$

$$= 36\,418 \text{ N} \quad (36 \text{ kN})$$

Answer is C.

20. Water flows steadily through the contraction shown.

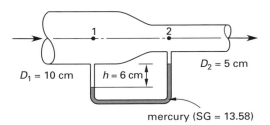

The velocity at section 1 is most nearly

(A) 1.0 m/s
(B) 1.4 m/s
(C) 1.8 m/s
(D) 2.2 m/s

Solution:

Bernoulli's equation is

$$\frac{p_1}{\rho_w g} + \frac{v_1^2}{2g} + z_1 = \frac{p_2}{\rho_w g} + \frac{v_2^2}{2g} + z_2$$

$$z_1 = z_2$$

$$v_2 = \left(\frac{D_1}{D_2}\right)^2 v_1 = \left(\frac{10 \text{ cm}}{5 \text{ cm}}\right)^2 v_1 = 4v_1$$

$$\frac{p_1 - p_2}{\rho_w g} = \frac{16v_1^2 - v_1^2}{2g} = \frac{15v_1^2}{2g}$$

$$p_1 - p_2 = hg(\rho_{\text{Hg}} - \rho_w)$$

$$\frac{p_1 - p_2}{\rho_w g} = \left(\frac{\rho_{\text{Hg}}}{\rho_w} - 1\right) h$$

$$\frac{15v_1^2}{2g} = \left(\frac{\rho_{\text{Hg}}}{\rho_w} - 1\right) h$$

$$v_1 = \sqrt{\left(\frac{2g}{15}\right)\left(\frac{\rho_{\text{Hg}}}{\rho_w} - 1\right) h}$$

$$= \sqrt{\left(\frac{(2)\left(9.81 \frac{\text{m}}{\text{s}^2}\right)}{15}\right)(13.58 - 1)(0.06 \text{ m})}$$

$$= 0.9936 \text{ m/s} \quad (1.0 \text{ m/s})$$

Answer is A.

21. Water flows in an inclined constant-diameter pipe. At point 1, $p_1 = 235$ kPa, and the elevation is $z_1 = 20$ m. At point 2, $p_2 = 200$ kPa, and $z_2 = 22$ m. The friction head loss between the two sections is most nearly

(A) 0.8 m
(B) 1.2 m
(C) 1.6 m
(D) 1.9 m

Solution:

$$\frac{p_1}{\rho g} + \frac{v_1^2}{2g} + z_1 = \frac{p_2}{\rho g} + \frac{v_2^2}{2g} + z_2 + h_{f_{1-2}}$$

$$v_1 = v_2$$

$$h_{f_{1-2}} = \frac{p_1 - p_2}{\rho g} + z_1 - z_2$$

$$= \frac{(235 \text{ kPa} - 200 \text{ kPa})\left(1000 \frac{\text{Pa}}{\text{kPa}}\right)}{\left(1000 \frac{\text{kg}}{\text{m}^3}\right)\left(9.81 \frac{\text{m}}{\text{s}^2}\right)}$$

$$+ 20 \text{ m} - 22 \text{ m}$$

$$= 1.568 \text{ m} \quad (1.6 \text{ m})$$

Answer is C.

22. Water at 32°C flows at 2 m/s in a pipe having an inside diameter of 3 cm. The viscosity of the water is 769×10^{-6} N·s/m^2, and the density is 995 kg/m^3. If the relative roughness of the pipe is 0.002, the friction factor is most nearly

(A) 0.025
(B) 0.030
(C) 0.035
(D) 0.040

Solution:

The kinematic viscosity is

$$\nu = \frac{\mu}{\rho} = \frac{769 \times 10^{-6} \frac{\text{N·s}}{\text{m}^2}}{995 \frac{\text{kg}}{\text{m}^3}} = 0.773 \times 10^{-6} \text{ m}^2/\text{s}$$

The Reynolds number is

$$\text{Re} = \frac{vD}{\nu} = \frac{\left(2 \frac{\text{m}}{\text{s}}\right)(0.03 \text{ m})}{0.773 \times 10^{-6} \frac{\text{m}^2}{\text{s}}}$$

$$= 77\,620 \quad [\text{turbulent flow}]$$

From the Moody diagram at Re $= 77\,600$ and $\epsilon/D = 0.002$, the friction factor is

$$f = 0.0254$$

Answer is A.

23. An airplane is traveling at 1900 km/h at an altitude where the temperature is $-60°C$. The Mach number at which the airplane is flying is most nearly

(A) 0.8
(B) 1.3
(C) 1.6
(D) 1.8

Solution:

$$c = \sqrt{kRT} = \sqrt{k\left(\frac{\overline{R}}{\text{MW}}\right)T}$$

$$= \sqrt{(1.4)\left(\frac{8314\ \dfrac{\text{J}}{\text{kmol·K}}}{29\ \dfrac{\text{kg}}{\text{kmol}}}\right)(-60°C + 273)}$$

$$= 292.4 \text{ m/s}$$

$$M = \frac{\text{v}}{c}$$

$$= \frac{\left(1900\ \dfrac{\text{km}}{\text{h}}\right)\left(1000\ \dfrac{\text{m}}{\text{km}}\right)\left(\dfrac{1}{3600\ \dfrac{\text{s}}{\text{h}}}\right)}{292.4\ \dfrac{\text{m}}{\text{s}}}$$

$$= 1.80$$

Answer is D.

HEAT TRANSFER

24. Heat flows steadily through a composite wall made up of two materials, A and B, of equal thickness. The thermal conductivity of material A is double that of material B.

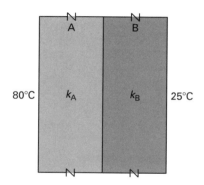

If the temperature of the outside surfaces of A and B are $80°C$ and $25°C$, respectively, the temperature of the contact surface is most nearly

(A) 54°C
(B) 58°C
(C) 62°C
(D) 66°C

Solution:

$$\dot{Q} = \frac{-k_A A(\Delta T)_A}{L_A} = \frac{-k_B A(\Delta T)_B}{L_B}$$

$$k_A = 2k_B$$

$$L_A = L_B$$

Therefore,

$$(\Delta T)_A = \frac{(\Delta T)_B}{2}$$

$$(2)(80°C - T) = T - 25°C$$

$$T = 61.7°C \quad (62°C)$$

Answer is C.

25. An 8 m long pipe of 15 cm outside diameter is covered with 2 cm of insulation with thermal conductivity of 0.09 W/m·K.

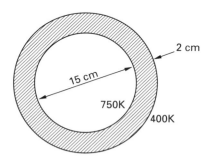

If the inner and outer temperatures of the insulation are 750K and 400K, respectively, what is the heat loss from the pipe?

(A) 4.5 kW
(B) 6.7 kW
(C) 8.5 kW
(D) 10 kW

Solution:

$$\dot{Q} = \frac{2\pi L k(T_1 - T_2)}{\ln\left(\dfrac{r_2}{r_1}\right)}$$

$$= \frac{2\pi(8\text{ m})\left(0.09\ \dfrac{\text{W}}{\text{m}\cdot\text{K}}\right)(750\text{K} - 400\text{K})}{\ln\left(\dfrac{9.5\text{ cm}}{7.5\text{ cm}}\right)}$$

$$= 6698\text{ W}\quad(6.7\text{ kW})$$

Answer is B.

26. Heat is generated internally at the rate of 1 MW/m^3 in a plane wall of thickness 0.07 m and thermal conductivity of 18 W/m·K. One side of the wall is insulated, and the other side is exposed to surroundings at 300K.

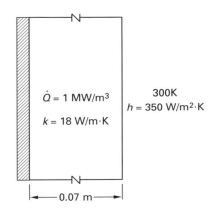

If the convective heat transfer coefficient between the wall and the surroundings is 350 W/m^2·K, the maximum temperature in the wall is likely to be

(A) 500K
(B) 550K
(C) 640K
(D) 700K

Solution:

The energy generated is equal to the convective heat loss.

$$\dot{Q}AL = hA(T_s - T_\infty)$$

$$T_s = \frac{\dot{Q}L}{h} + T_\infty$$

$$= \frac{\left(10^6\ \dfrac{\text{W}}{\text{m}^3}\right)(0.07\text{ m})}{350\ \dfrac{\text{W}}{\text{m}^2\cdot\text{K}}} + 300\text{K}$$

$$= 500\text{K}$$

The maximum temperature occurs at the insulated surface and is given by

$$T_{\max} = T_s + \left(\frac{\dot{Q}}{2k}\right)L^2$$

$$= 500\text{K} + \left(\frac{10^6\ \dfrac{\text{W}}{\text{m}^3}}{(2)\left(18\ \dfrac{\text{W}}{\text{m}\cdot\text{K}}\right)}\right)(0.07\text{ m})^2$$

$$= 636\text{K}\quad(640\text{K})$$

Answer is C.

27. An electrically heated plate is mounted vertically in 25°C air. The plate has a surface area of 0.1 m^2, has a height of 0.3 m, and is maintained at a uniform temperature of 130°C.

Assume the kinematic viscosity of air is 20.92×10^{-6} m^2/s, the thermal conductivity is 30×10^{-3} W/m·K, and the Prandtl number is 0.7. The power dissipation is most nearly

(A) 45 W
(B) 60 W
(C) 66 W
(D) 74 W

Solution:

$$T_s = 130°\text{C} + 273 = 403\text{K}$$

$$T_\infty = 25°\text{C} + 273 = 298\text{K}$$

The coefficient of volumetric expansion is the reciprocal of the absolute temperature of the film, which is the average of the surface and local temperatures.

$$\beta = \frac{2}{T_s + T_\infty} = \frac{2}{403\text{K} + 298\text{K}} = 0.00285\text{K}^{-1}$$

The Rayleigh number is,

$$\text{Ra} = \frac{g\beta(T_s - T_\infty)L^3\text{Pr}}{\nu^2}$$

$$= \frac{\left(9.81\ \dfrac{\text{m}}{\text{s}^2}\right)(0.00285\text{K}^{-1})}{\left(20.92 \times 10^{-6}\ \dfrac{\text{m}}{\text{s}^2}\right)^2}$$
$$\times (403\text{K} - 298\text{K})(0.3\text{ m})^3(0.7)$$

$$= 1.27 \times 10^8$$

At this value of Ra, $C = 0.59$ and $n = 1/4$. The heat transfer coefficient is

$$h = C \left(\frac{k}{L}\right) \mathrm{Ra}^n$$

$$= (0.59) \left(\frac{30 \times 10^{-3} \dfrac{\mathrm{W}}{\mathrm{m \cdot K}}}{0.3 \ \mathrm{m}}\right) (1.27 \times 10^8)^{\frac{1}{4}}$$

$$= 6.26 \ \mathrm{W/m^2 \cdot K}$$

$$\dot{Q} = hA\Delta T$$

$$= \left(6.26 \ \frac{\mathrm{W}}{\mathrm{m^2 \cdot K}}\right)(0.1 \ \mathrm{m^2})(130^\circ\mathrm{C} - 25^\circ\mathrm{C})$$

$$= 65.7 \ \mathrm{W} \quad (66 \ \mathrm{W})$$

Answer is C.

---

28. Water at a bulk temperature of 300K flows inside a long hot pipe of 3 cm ID and at a velocity of 1.3 m/s. At 300K, water properties are

$$v = 1.003 \times 10^{-3} \ \mathrm{m^3/kg}$$
$$c_p = 4.178 \ \mathrm{kJ/kg \cdot K}$$
$$\mu = 855 \times 10^{-6} \ \mathrm{N \cdot s/m^2}$$
$$k = 613 \times 10^{-3} \ \mathrm{W/m \cdot K}$$
$$\mathrm{Pr} = 5.83$$

The heat transfer coefficient is most nearly

(A) 2 kW/m²·K
(B) 3 kW/m²·K
(C) 4 kW/m²·K
(D) 5 kW/m²·K

Solution:

$$\mathrm{Re} = \frac{\rho v D}{\mu}$$

$$= \frac{\left(\dfrac{1}{1.003 \times 10^{-3} \dfrac{\mathrm{m^3}}{\mathrm{kg}}}\right)\left(1.3 \ \dfrac{\mathrm{m}}{\mathrm{s}}\right)(0.03 \ \mathrm{m})}{855 \times 10^{-6} \ \dfrac{\mathrm{N \cdot s}}{\mathrm{m^2}}}$$

$$= 45\,478 \quad [\text{turbulent flow}]$$

$$\mathrm{Nu} = 0.023 \ \mathrm{Re}^{0.8} \mathrm{Pr}^{0.4}$$

$$= (0.023)(45\,478)^{0.8}(5.83)^{0.4}$$

$$= 247.9$$

$$h = \mathrm{Nu} \left(\frac{k}{D}\right)$$

$$= (247.9) \left(\frac{613 \times 10^{-3} \ \dfrac{\mathrm{W}}{\mathrm{m \cdot K}}}{0.03 \ \mathrm{m}}\right)$$

$$= 5065 \ \mathrm{W/m^2 \cdot K} \quad (5 \ \mathrm{kW/m^2 \cdot K})$$

Answer is D.

---

29. A hot 2 cm diameter metal sphere radiates to a low-temperature enclosure. If 12 W of power is needed to maintain the sphere at 1000K, the emmisivity of the sphere is most nearly

(A) 0.17
(B) 0.2
(C) 0.25
(D) 0.27

Solution:

$$E = \frac{\dot{Q}}{A} = \frac{12 \ \mathrm{W}}{\pi D^2}$$

$$E_b = \sigma T^4$$

$$\epsilon = \frac{E}{E_b} = \frac{\dfrac{12 \ \mathrm{W}}{\pi (0.02 \ \mathrm{m})^2}}{\left(5.67 \times 10^{-8} \ \dfrac{\mathrm{W}}{\mathrm{m^2 \cdot K^4}}\right)(1000\mathrm{K})^4}$$

$$= 0.168 \quad (0.17)$$

Answer is A.

MATERIAL BEHAVIOR AND PROCESSING

30. Aluminum has a face-centered cubic (FCC) unit cell structure with a lattice constant of 0.405 nm. The density of aluminum is most nearly

(A) 0.7 g/cm³
(B) 1.3 g/cm³
(C) 2.7 g/cm³
(D) 5.4 g/cm³

Solution:

$$\rho = \frac{m}{V} = \frac{(\text{no. of atoms per cell})(\mathrm{MW})}{\text{volume of cell}}$$

$$= \frac{\left(4 \ \dfrac{\mathrm{atoms}}{\mathrm{cell}}\right)\left(26.981 \ \dfrac{\mathrm{kg}}{\mathrm{kmol}}\right)\left(\dfrac{1}{1000} \ \dfrac{\mathrm{kmol}}{\mathrm{mol}}\right)}{\left(6.022 \times 10^{23} \ \dfrac{\mathrm{atoms}}{\mathrm{mol}}\right)(0.405 \times 10^{-9} \ \mathrm{m})^3}$$

$$= 2698 \ \mathrm{kg/m^3} \quad (2.7 \ \mathrm{g/cm^3})$$

Answer is C.

31. The diffusivity of nickel atoms in a solid FCC iron lattice is 1.0×10^{-13} m²/s at 1300°C and 1.0×10^{-16} m²/s at 1000°C. The average activation energy for the diffusion of Ni atoms in the FCC iron lattice is most nearly

(A) 280 kJ/mol
(B) 380 kJ/mol
(C) 580 kJ/mol
(D) 880 kJ/mol

Solution:

$$D = D_0 e^{-\frac{Q}{RT}}$$

$$\frac{D_1}{D_2} = \frac{e^{-\frac{Q}{RT_1}}}{e^{-\frac{Q}{RT_2}}} = e^{\left(\frac{Q}{R}\right)\left(\frac{-1}{T_1} + \frac{1}{T_2}\right)}$$

$$T_1 = 1300°C + 273 = 1573K$$
$$T_2 = 1000°C + 273 = 1273K$$

$$Q = \left(\frac{\overline{R}}{\frac{-1}{T_1} + \frac{1}{T_2}}\right) \ln\left(\frac{D_1}{D_2}\right)$$

$$= \left(\frac{8.314 \, \frac{J}{mol \cdot K}}{\frac{-1}{1573K} + \frac{1}{1273K}}\right) \ln\left(\frac{10^{-13} \, \frac{m^2}{s}}{10^{-16} \, \frac{m^2}{s}}\right)$$

$$= 3.83 \times 10^5 \, J/mol \quad (380 \, kJ/mol)$$

Answer is B.

32. 454 g of solder, made of 90% lead (Pb) and 10% tin (Sn), are to be completely liquified at 200°C by the addition of more tin.

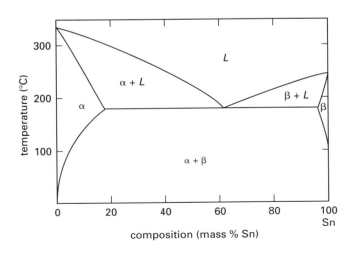

The minimum amount of tin that must be added per 100 g of solder is most nearly

(A) 114 g
(B) 125 g
(C) 140 g
(D) 165 g

Solution:

Initially,

$$m_{Sn} = (0.1)(454 \, g) = 45.4 \, g$$

Let x equal the amount of Sn added.

From the figure, at 200°C solder liquifies at approximately 58% Sn.

$$0.58 = \frac{m_{Sn}}{m_{solder}} = \frac{45.4 \, g + x}{454 \, g + x}$$

$$x = 518.9 \, g \text{ of Sn per } 454 \, g \text{ solder}$$

$$m_{Sn} \text{ per } 100 \, g \text{ solder} = \left(\frac{518.9 \, g}{454 \, g}\right)(100 \, g)$$

$$= 114.3 \, g \quad (114 \, g)$$

Answer is A.

MEASUREMENT AND INSTRUMENTATION

33. A pitot tube is used to measure the velocity of an air stream. The air is at a temperature of 18°C and a pressure of 105 kPa.

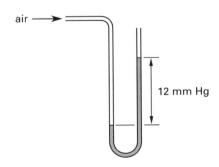

If the differential height in a mercury manometer is 12 mm and the air is incompressible, the air velocity is most nearly

(A) 38 m/s
(B) 43 m/s
(C) 48 m/s
(D) 50 m/s

Solution:

$$\rho_{air} = \frac{p}{RT} = \frac{105 \text{ kPa}}{\left(0.287\frac{\text{kJ}}{\text{kg·K}}\right)(18°C + 273)}$$

$$= 1.2572 \text{ kg/m}^3$$

$$\rho_{Hg} = 13\,550 \text{ kg/m}^3$$

$$\Delta p = \rho_{air}\left(\frac{v^2}{2}\right) = (\rho_{Hg} - \rho_{air})gh$$

$$v = \sqrt{\frac{2\Delta p}{\rho_{air}}} = \sqrt{2\left(\frac{\rho_{Hg}}{\rho_{air}} - 1\right)gh}$$

$$= \sqrt{(2)\left(\frac{13\,550\,\frac{\text{kg}}{\text{m}^3}}{1.2572\,\frac{\text{kg}}{\text{m}^3}} - 1\right)\left(9.81\,\frac{\text{m}}{\text{s}^2}\right)(0.012 \text{ m})}$$

$$= 50.37 \text{ m/s} (50 \text{ m/s})$$

Answer is D.

---

34. An oil with a specific gravity of 0.92 is in a tank pressurized to 25 kPa. The oil flows through a sharp orifice with a diameter of 1 cm, 3 m below the oil surface.

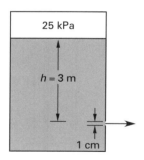

If the coefficient of discharge is 0.72, the discharge rate is most nearly

(A) $4 \times 10^{-4} \text{ m}^3/\text{s}$

(B) $6 \times 10^{-4} \text{ m}^3/\text{s}$

(C) $8 \times 10^{-4} \text{ m}^3/\text{s}$

(D) $10 \times 10^{-4} \text{ m}^3/\text{s}$

Solution:

$$Q = C_d A\sqrt{2g\left(h + \frac{p}{\rho g}\right)}$$

$$= (0.72)\left(\frac{\pi}{4}\right)(0.01 \text{ m})^2$$

$$\times \sqrt{\frac{(2)\left(9.81\,\frac{\text{m}}{\text{s}^2}\right)}{\times\left(3\text{ m} + \frac{(25 \text{ kPa})\left(1000\,\frac{\text{Pa}}{\text{kPa}}\right)}{(0.92)\left(1000\,\frac{\text{kg}}{\text{m}^3}\right)\left(9.81\,\frac{\text{m}}{\text{s}^2}\right)}\right)}}$$

$$= 6.02 \times 10^{-4} \text{ m}^3/\text{s} (6 \times 10^{-4} \text{ m}^3/\text{s})$$

Answer is B.

---

35. Water flows through a venturi meter as shown.

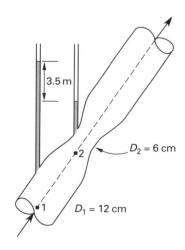

If the static pressure difference between sections 1 and 2 is 3.5 m of water and the coefficient of velocity is 0.98, the volumetric flow rate is most nearly

(A) $0.012 \text{ m}^3/\text{s}$

(B) $0.018 \text{ m}^3/\text{s}$

(C) $0.024 \text{ m}^3/\text{s}$

(D) $0.030 \text{ m}^3/\text{s}$

Solution:

$$Q = \frac{C_{\mathrm{v}} A_2}{\sqrt{1 - \left(\frac{A_2}{A_1}\right)^2}} \sqrt{2g\left(\frac{\Delta p}{\rho g}\right)}$$

$$= C_{\mathrm{v}}\left(\frac{\pi}{4}\right) D_2^2 \sqrt{\frac{2g\left(\frac{\rho g \Delta h}{\rho g}\right)}{1 - \left(\frac{D_2}{D_1}\right)^4}}$$

$$= (0.98)\left(\frac{\pi}{4}\right)(0.06\ \mathrm{m})^2 \sqrt{\frac{(2)\left(9.81\ \frac{\mathrm{m}}{\mathrm{s}^2}\right)(3.5\ \mathrm{m})}{1 - \left(\frac{0.06\ \mathrm{m}}{0.12\ \mathrm{m}}\right)^4}}$$

$$= 0.0237\ \mathrm{m}^3/\mathrm{s} \quad (0.024\ \mathrm{m}^3/\mathrm{s})$$

Answer is C.

36. Water flows upward through an 8 cm×4 cm venturi meter as shown. The differential manometer deflection is 50 cm of liquid of specific gravity 1.3.

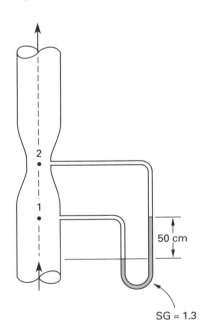

If the coefficient of velocity is 0.95, the flow rate is most nearly

(A) 0.0010 m³/s
(B) 0.0012 m³/s
(C) 0.0015 m³/s
(D) 0.0021 m³/s

Solution:

$$\frac{\Delta p}{\rho_w} = \frac{(\rho_m - \rho_w)\Delta h}{\rho_w} = (\mathrm{SG}_m - 1)\Delta h$$

$$= (1.3 - 1)\left(\frac{50\ \mathrm{cm}}{100\ \frac{\mathrm{cm}}{\mathrm{m}}}\right)$$

$$= 0.15\ \mathrm{m}$$

$$Q = C_{\mathrm{v}} A_2 \sqrt{\frac{2g\left(\frac{\Delta p}{\rho_w g}\right)}{1 - \left(\frac{A_2}{A_1}\right)^2}}$$

$$= (0.95)\left(\frac{\pi}{4}\right)(0.04\ \mathrm{m})^2 \sqrt{\frac{(2)\left(9.81\ \frac{\mathrm{m}}{\mathrm{s}^2}\right)(0.15\ \mathrm{m})}{1 - \left(\frac{4\ \mathrm{cm}}{8\ \mathrm{cm}}\right)^4}}$$

$$= 0.00212\ \mathrm{m}^3/\mathrm{s} \quad (0.0021\ \mathrm{m}^3/\mathrm{s})$$

Answer is D.

37. Air flows adiabatically at the rate of 0.1 kg/s through a 3 cm diameter tube. At one location, the static and stagnation temperatures are 300K and 320K, respectively. The static pressure at the same location is most nearly

(A) 25 kPa
(B) 50 kPa
(C) 61 kPa
(D) 70 kPa

Solution:

The stagnation enthalpy is

$$h_0 = h + \frac{\mathrm{v}^2}{2}$$

$$\mathrm{v} = \sqrt{2(h_0 - h)} = \sqrt{2c_p(T_0 - T)}$$

$$= \sqrt{(2)\left(1003.5\ \frac{\mathrm{J}}{\mathrm{kg\cdot K}}\right)(320\mathrm{K} - 300\mathrm{K})}$$

$$= 200.3\ \mathrm{m/s}$$

$$\rho = \frac{\dot{m}}{A\mathrm{v}} = \frac{0.1\ \frac{\mathrm{kg}}{\mathrm{s}}}{\left(\frac{\pi}{4}\right)(0.03\ \mathrm{m})^2\left(200.3\ \frac{\mathrm{m}}{\mathrm{s}}\right)}$$

$$= 0.7063\ \mathrm{kg/m}^3$$

$p = \rho RT$

$$= \left(0.7063 \; \frac{\text{kg}}{\text{m}^3}\right)\left(0.287 \; \frac{\text{kJ}}{\text{kg·K}}\right)(300\text{K})$$

$$= 60.8 \text{ kPa} \quad (61 \text{ kPa})$$

Answer is C.

38. An error of 0.8 kPa was discovered in reading the velocity head of a liquid flowing at a velocity of 1.6 m/s. What would be the corresponding error in the pressure if the velocity were 3 m/s?

    (A) 1.6 kPa
    (B) 2.0 kPa
    (C) 2.4 kPa
    (D) 2.8 kPa

Solution:

The velocity head is proportional to the square of velocity.

$$\frac{E_2}{E_1} = \frac{\text{v}_2^2}{\text{v}_1^2}$$

$$E_2 = (E_1)\left(\frac{\text{v}_2}{\text{v}_1}\right)^2 = (0.8 \text{ kPa})\left(\frac{3 \; \frac{\text{m}}{\text{s}}}{1.6 \; \frac{\text{m}}{\text{s}}}\right)^2$$

$$= 2.81 \text{ kPa} \quad (2.8 \text{ kPa})$$

Answer is D.

MECHANICAL DESIGN

39. A cantilever beam with a rectangular cross section is subjected to an inclined force as shown.

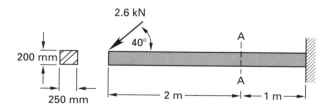

The maximum bending stress at section A-A is most nearly

    (A) 0.6 MPa
    (B) 1.4 MPa
    (C) 2.1 MPa
    (D) 2.6 MPa

Solution:

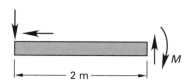

This is an eccentric stress.

$$M_{\text{A-A}} = (2.6 \text{ kN})(\sin 40°)(2 \text{ m})$$
$$+ (2.6 \text{ kN})(\cos 40°)(0.1 \text{ m})$$
$$= 3.54 \text{ kN·m}$$

$$\sigma_{\max} = \frac{Mc}{I} = \frac{Mc}{\frac{1}{12}bh^3} = \frac{(3.54 \times 10^3 \text{ N·m})(0.1 \text{ m})}{\left(\frac{1}{12}\right)(0.25 \text{ m})(0.2 \text{ m})^3}$$

$$= 2.12 \times 10^6 \text{ Pa} \quad (2.1 \text{ MPa})$$

Answer is C.

40. A rectangular timber 10 cm wide by 25 cm thick is used as a cantilever beam to carry a uniform load of 200 kg/m, which includes the weight of the beam. The allowable tensile stress is 20 kPa, and shear failure is not a concern. Neglect buckling.

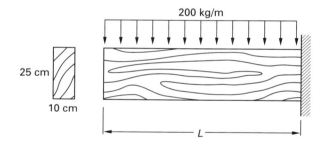

The maximum length of the beam is most nearly

    (A) 0.15 m
    (B) 1.50 m
    (C) 2.00 m
    (D) 2.75 m

Solution:

For the purpose of finding the maximum moment the distributed load can be considered as a concentrated load located at the centroid of the load area.

$$V = mgL = \left(200 \; \frac{\text{kg}}{\text{m}}\right)\left(9.81 \; \frac{\text{m}}{\text{s}^2}\right)L = 1962L$$

The maximum moment, which occurs at the built-in end, is

$$M = \frac{VL}{2} = \frac{1962L^2}{2}$$

The maximum tensile flexural stress is

$$\sigma_{\max} = \frac{Mc}{I} = \frac{\left(\dfrac{1962L^2}{2}\right)\left(\dfrac{h}{2}\right)}{\dfrac{bh^3}{12}}$$

$$L = \sqrt{\frac{bh^2\sigma_{\max}}{(3)(1962)}}$$

$$= \sqrt{\frac{(0.10 \text{ m})(0.25 \text{ m})^2(20 \times 10^3 \text{ Pa})}{(3)\left(1962 \dfrac{\text{N}}{\text{m}}\right)}}$$

$$= 0.146 \text{ m} \quad (0.15 \text{ m})$$

Answer is A.

41. A slender round column is to be designed to carry a maximum axial load of 15 kN. The column is fixed at one end and free at the other, with a total free length of 0.5 m. The modulus of elasticity and the yield strength are 200 GPa and 700 MPa, respectively. The design factor of safety is 3.5.

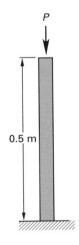

The minimum column diameter is most nearly

(A) 10 mm
(B) 20 mm
(C) 30 mm
(D) 40 mm

Solution:

The design load is the critical buckling load.

$$P_{\mathrm{cr}} = (\mathrm{FS})P = (3.5)(15 \text{ kN}) = 52.5 \text{ kN}$$
$$= \frac{\pi^2 EI}{k^2 \ell^2}$$

$$I = \left(\frac{\pi}{64}\right)d^4$$

$$d = \left(\frac{64k^2\ell^2 P_{\mathrm{cr}}}{\pi^3 E}\right)^{\frac{1}{4}}$$

$$= \left(\frac{(64)(2.1)^2(0.5 \text{ m})^2(52.5 \times 10^3 \text{ N})}{\pi^3(200 \times 10^9 \text{ Pa})}\right)^{\frac{1}{4}}$$

$$= 0.0278 \text{ m} \quad (30 \text{ mm})$$

$$\sigma = \frac{P}{A} = \frac{52.2 \times 10^3 \text{ N}}{\left(\dfrac{\pi}{4}\right)(0.0278 \text{ m})^2} = 8.6 \times 10^7$$

$$= 86 \text{ MPa} < \left(\frac{1}{2}\right)(700 \text{ MPa}) \quad [\text{OK}]$$

Answer is C.

42. A round cantilever beam carries a vertical tip load of 2 kN, an axial tensile force of 10 kN, and a torque of 50 N·m. The length and diameter of the beam are 15 cm and 5 cm, respectively.

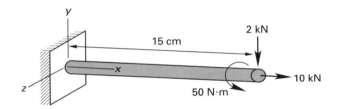

The maximum shear stress is most nearly

(A) 1 MPa
(B) 5 MPa
(C) 10 MPa
(D) 15 MPa

Solution:

$$M = FL = (2 \text{ kN})(15 \text{ cm})\left(\frac{1 \text{ m}}{100 \text{ cm}}\right)$$

$$= 0.3 \text{ kN·m}$$

$$\tau_{\max} = \left(\frac{2}{\pi d^3}\right)\left((8M + Fd)^2 + (8T)^2\right)^{\frac{1}{2}}$$

$$= \left(\frac{2}{\pi(0.05 \text{ m})^3}\right)$$

$$\times \left(\begin{pmatrix}(8)(0.3 \times 10^3 \text{ N·m}) \\ + (10 \times 10^3 \text{ N})(0.05 \text{ m})\end{pmatrix}^2 + (8)^2(50 \text{ N·m})^2\right)^{\frac{1}{2}}$$

$$= 1.49 \times 10^7 \text{ Pa} \quad (15 \text{ MPa})$$

Answer is D.

43. The simply supported beam shown is uniformly loaded at 500 N/m. The length of the beam is 2 m.

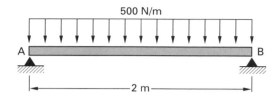

The maximum moment on the beam is most nearly

(A) 0 N·m
(B) 250 N·m
(C) 500 N·m
(D) 1000 N·m

Solution:

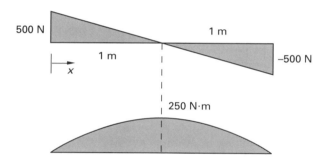

Due to symmetry,

$$R_A = R_B = \frac{(2 \text{ m})\left(500\ \dfrac{\text{N}}{\text{m}}\right)}{2} = 500 \text{ N}$$

The shear is

$$V = 500 - 500x$$

The moment over one-half of the beam is

$$M_{\max} = \int V \, dx = \int_0^1 (500 - 500x) \, dx$$

$$= \left| 500x - 250x^2 \right|_0^1$$

$$= (500 \text{ N})(1 \text{ m}) - \left(250\ \frac{\text{N}}{\text{m}}\right)(1 \text{ m})^2 - 0 + 0$$

$$= 250 \text{ N·m}$$

Answer is B.

44. A beam of rectangular cross section is supported and loaded as shown. How far from point A is the point of zero shear?

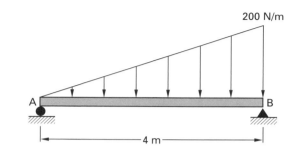

(A) 1.8 m
(B) 2.3 m
(C) 2.8 m
(D) 3.1 m

Solution:

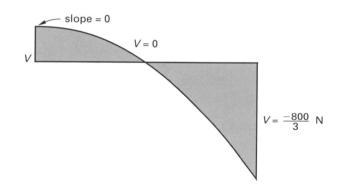

$$\sum M_A = 0:$$

$$R_B(4 \text{ m}) - \left(\frac{1}{2}\right)\left(200\ \frac{\text{N}}{\text{m}}\right)(4 \text{ m})(4 \text{ m})\left(\frac{2}{3}\right) = 0$$

$$R_B = \frac{800}{3} \text{ N}$$

$$R_A = \left(\frac{1}{2}\right)\left(200\ \frac{\text{N}}{\text{m}}\right)(4 \text{ m}) - \frac{800}{3} \text{ N} = \frac{400}{3} \text{ N}$$

$$\sum F_y = 0:$$

$$\frac{400}{3} \text{ N} - \left(\frac{1}{2}\right)\left(200\ \frac{\text{N}}{\text{m}}\right)\left(\frac{x}{4 \text{ m}}\right)x = 0$$

$$x = 2.31 \text{ m}$$

Answer is B.

REFRIGERATION AND HVAC

45. An ideal vapor-compression refrigeration cycle uses R-134a as a refrigerant. The cycle operates between 0.1 MPa and 0.7 MPa. If the flow rate of the refrigerant is 0.15 kg/s, the rate of heat transfer in the evaporator is most nearly

    (A) 14 kW
    (B) 18 kW
    (C) 22 kW
    (D) 26 kW

Solution:

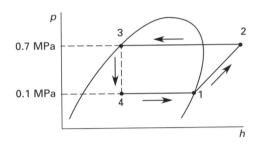

At $p_1 = 0.1$ MPa, $h_1 = h_{g_1} = 382.8$ kJ/kg. At $p_3 = 0.7$ MPa, $h_3 = h_4 = h_{f_3} = 237.0$ kJ/kg.

$$\dot{Q} = \dot{m}(h_1 - h_4)$$

$$= \left(0.15 \ \frac{\text{kg}}{\text{s}}\right)\left(382.8 \ \frac{\text{kJ}}{\text{kg}} - 237.0 \ \frac{\text{kJ}}{\text{kg}}\right)$$

$$= 21.87 \ \text{kW} \quad (22 \ \text{kW})$$

Answer is C.

46. Air enters the compressor of an ideal-gas refrigeration open cycle at 25°C and 1 atm and is compressed isentropically to 3 atm. The air is then cooled to 75°C before expanding isentropically to 1 atm in a turbine. If the air flow rate is 0.1 kg/s, what is the net power input to the cycle?

    (A) 1.2 kW
    (B) 1.3 kW
    (C) 1.5 kW
    (D) 1.6 kW

Solution:

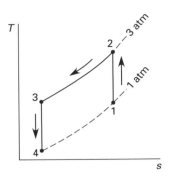

With isentropic compression and expansion in the compressor and turbine,

$$T_2 = T_1 \left(\frac{p_2}{p_1}\right)^{\frac{k-1}{k}}$$

$$= (25°\text{C} + 273)\left(\frac{3 \ \text{atm}}{1 \ \text{atm}}\right)^{\frac{1.4-1}{1.4}}$$

$$= 407.9\text{K}$$

$$T_4 = T_3 \left(\frac{p_4}{p_3}\right)^{\frac{k-1}{k}}$$

$$= (75°\text{C} + 273)\left(\frac{1 \ \text{atm}}{3 \ \text{atm}}\right)^{\frac{1.4-1}{1.4}}$$

$$= 254.2\text{K}$$

The net power input is

$$\dot{W} = \dot{m}\big((h_2 - h_1) - (h_3 - h_4)\big)$$

$$= \dot{m}c_p\big((T_2 - T_1) - (T_3 - T_4)\big)$$

$$= \left(0.1 \ \frac{\text{kg}}{\text{s}}\right)\left(1.0035 \ \frac{\text{kJ}}{\text{kg·K}}\right)$$

$$\times (407.9\text{K} - 298\text{K} - 348\text{K} + 254.2\text{K})$$

$$= 1.62 \ \text{kW}$$

Answer is D.

47. A thermoelectric refrigerator removes 100 W of energy from a refrigerated space maintained at −2°C. It rejects energy to an environment at 27°C. The minimum input power required is

    (A) 5 W
    (B) 8 W
    (C) 11 W
    (D) 13 W

Solution:

The maximum (ideal) coefficient of performance is

$$\text{COP} = \frac{\dot{Q}_L}{\dot{W}} = \frac{T_L}{T_H - T_L} = \frac{-2°\text{C} + 273}{27°\text{C} - (-2°\text{C})}$$

$$= 9.34$$

$$\dot{W} = \frac{\dot{Q}_L}{\text{COP}} = \frac{100 \text{ W}}{9.34}$$

$$= 10.7 \text{ W} \quad (11 \text{ W})$$

Answer is C.

48. The temperature of a glass window in a room is 15°C. If the air temperature in the room is 25°C, the maximum relative humidity before condensation occurs on the glass is most nearly

(A) 35%
(B) 45%
(C) 55%
(D) 65%

Solution:

During the sensible coding process from 1 to 2, ω and p_v remain constant.

At state 2, $\phi_2 = 100\%$ so that

$$p_{v,2} = (p_{v,\text{sat}})_{15°\text{C}} = 1.7051 \text{ kPa}$$

$$\phi_2 = \frac{p_{v,2}}{(p_{v,\text{sat}})_{25°\text{C}}} = \frac{1.7051 \text{ kPa}}{3.169 \text{ kPa}}$$

$$= 0.538 \quad (55\%)$$

This can also be found graphically on the psychrometric chart.

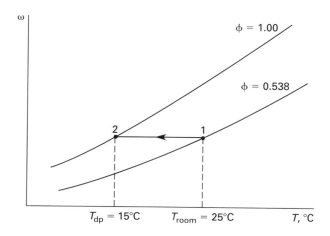

Answer is C.

49. Outside air at a pressure of 101 kPa, a temperature of 10°C, and a relative humidity of 70% is heated to a temperature of 25°C. If the incoming volumetric flow rate is 1 m^3/s, the rate of heat transfer is most nearly

(A) 8 kW
(B) 11 kW
(C) 15 kW
(D) 19 kW

Solution:

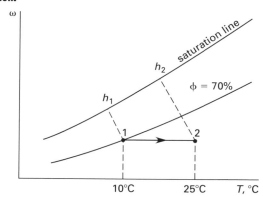

From the psychrometric chart at $T_1 = 10°\text{C}$ and $\phi_1 = 70\%$,

$$h_1 = 23.6 \text{ kJ/kg of dry air}$$

During the heating process the specific humidity, ω, remains constant.

Following a horizontal line to 25°C, determine state 2.

From the chart, $h_2 = 39$ kJ/kg of dry air.

At 10°C,

$$p_{v,\text{sat}} = 1.2276 \text{ kPa}$$
$$p_v = \phi p_{v,\text{sat}} = (0.7)(1.2276 \text{ kPa}) = 0.859 \text{ kPa}$$
$$p_a = 101 \text{ kPa} - 0.859 \text{ kPa} = 100.1 \text{ kPa}$$

The mass flow rate of the dry air is

$$\dot{m}_a = \frac{p_a V_a}{R_a T_a} = \frac{(100.1 \text{ kPa})\left(1.0 \frac{\text{m}^3}{\text{s}}\right)}{\left(0.287 \frac{\text{kJ}}{\text{kg·K}}\right)(10°\text{C} + 273)}$$

$$= 1.23 \text{ kg/s}$$

$$\dot{Q} = \dot{m}_a(h_2 - h_1)$$

$$= \left(1.23 \frac{\text{kg}}{\text{s}}\right)\left(39 \frac{\text{kJ}}{\text{kg}} - 23.6 \frac{\text{kJ}}{\text{kg}}\right)$$

$$= 18.9 \text{ kW} \quad (19 \text{ kW})$$

Answer is D.

STRESS ANALYSIS

50. A bolt of 25 mm diameter is used to suspend a load. The bolt is supported by a timber beam as shown. The maximum tensile stress developed in the bolt is 83 MPa. A rigid circular steel washer is used to lower the bearing stress on the beam to a maximum value of 3.4 MPa. The bolt fits snugly through the washer.

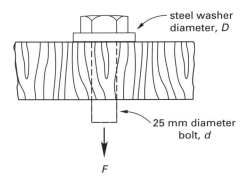

The minumum diameter for the circular washer should be most nearly

(A) 75 mm
(B) 100 mm
(C) 125 mm
(D) 150 mm

Solution:

$$F = \sigma_{\text{bolt}} A_{\text{bolt}} = \sigma_{\text{bolt}} \left(\frac{\pi}{4}\right) d^2$$

$$= \left(83 \times 10^6 \ \frac{\text{N}}{\text{m}^2}\right)\left(\frac{\pi}{4}\right)(0.025 \ \text{m})^2$$

$$= 40\,743 \ \text{N}$$

$$A_{\text{bearing}} = \frac{F}{\sigma_{\text{bearing}}} = \frac{40\,743 \ \text{N}}{3.4 \times 10^6 \ \frac{\text{N}}{\text{m}^2}}$$

$$= 1.198 \times 10^{-2} \ \text{m}^2$$

The net contact bearing area is

$$A_{\text{net}} = \left(\frac{\pi}{4}\right) D^2 - \left(\frac{\pi}{4}\right) d^2$$

Assume the washer hole diameter is the same as the bolt diameter.

$$1.198 \times 10^{-2} \ \text{m}^2 = \left(\frac{\pi}{4}\right) D^2 - \left(\frac{\pi}{4}\right)(0.025 \ \text{m})^2$$

$$D = 0.126 \ \text{m} \quad (125 \ \text{mm})$$

Answer is C.

51. Three aluminum bar segments, A, B, and C, are loaded as shown. The diameters of segments A and B are 2.5 cm and 4 cm, respectively, and the cross section of segment C is 5 cm by 5 cm.

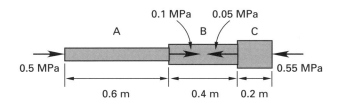

The total ideal deformation of the entire system is most nearly

(A) 0.001 m
(B) 0.005 m
(C) 0.010 m
(D) 0.020 m

Solution:

The free-body diagrams are as follows.

Segment A:

Segment B:

Segment C:

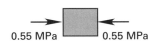

Areas:

$$A_{\text{A}} = \left(\frac{\pi}{4}\right) D_{\text{A}}^2 = \left(\frac{\pi}{4}\right)(0.025 \ \text{m})^2 = 4.91 \times 10^{-4} \ \text{m}^2$$

$$A_{\text{B}} = \left(\frac{\pi}{4}\right) D_{\text{B}}^2 = \left(\frac{\pi}{4}\right)(0.040 \ \text{m})^2 = 1.26 \times 10^{-3} \ \text{m}^2$$

$$A_{\text{C}} = (0.05 \ \text{m})(0.05 \ \text{m}) = 2.5 \times 10^{-3} \ \text{m}^2$$

The total compression is $\delta = \delta_{\text{A}} + \delta_{\text{B}} + \delta_{\text{C}}$.

$$\delta = \sum \frac{P_i L_i}{A_i E_i}$$

For aluminum, $E = 69$ GPa.

$$\delta = \left(\frac{(0.5 \times 10^6 \text{ Pa})(0.6 \text{ m})}{4.91 \times 10^{-4} \text{ m}} + \frac{(0.6 \times 10^6 \text{ Pa})(0.4 \text{ m})}{1.26 \times 10^{-3} \text{ m}} \right.$$
$$\left. + \frac{(0.55 \times 10^6 \text{ Pa})(0.2 \text{ m})}{2.5 \times 10^{-3} \text{ m}} \right)$$
$$\times \left(\frac{1}{69 \times 10^9 \text{ Pa}} \right)$$
$$= 0.0123 \text{ m} \quad (0.010 \text{ m})$$

Answer is C.

52. A bar of length 1.0 m is placed horizontally as shown. The gap between the right end of the bar and the rigid right wall is 0.5 mm. The coefficient of thermal expansion, α, and the modulus of elasticity of the bar are 20×10^{-6} 1/°C and 120 GPa, respectively.

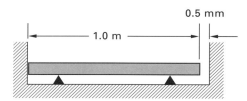

If the temperature of only the bar is raised by 100°C, the axial compressive stress produced in the bar as a result of elongation will most nearly be

(A) 50 MPa
(B) 75 MPa
(C) 120 MPa
(D) 180 MPa

Solution:

The unconfined elongation due to the temperature rise is
$$\delta = \alpha \Delta T L$$
$$= \left(20 \times 10^{-6} \, \frac{1}{\text{°C}} \right) (100\text{°C})(1 \text{ m})$$
$$= 2 \times 10^{-3} \text{ m} \quad (2 \text{ mm})$$

The compression is
$$\delta_c = \delta - 0.5 \text{ mm} = 2 \text{ mm} - 0.5 \text{ mm}$$
$$= 1.5 \text{ mm}$$

The compressive force is
$$F_c = \frac{\delta_c A E}{L}$$

The compressive stress is
$$\sigma_c = \frac{F_c}{A} = \frac{\delta_c E}{L} = \frac{(0.0015 \text{ m})(120 \times 10^9 \text{ Pa})}{1.0 \text{ m} + 0.0005 \text{ m}}$$
$$= 1.80 \times 10^8 \text{ Pa} \quad (180 \text{ MPa})$$

Answer is D.

53. A 10 m long solid steel shaft transmits 75 kW. The maximum shear stress and shear modulus of the shaft are 55 MPa and 80 GPa, respectively. The shaft rotates at a constant speed of 2000 rpm. The angle of twist of the shaft over its full length is most nearly

(A) 10°
(B) 15°
(C) 25°
(D) 35°

Solution:

$$T = \frac{P}{2\pi\omega} = \frac{(60)(75 \times 10^3 \text{ W})}{2\pi \left(2000 \, \frac{\text{rev}}{\text{min}} \right)} = 358.1 \text{ N·m}$$

The polar moment of inertia is

$$J = \frac{\pi d^4}{32}$$

The radial distance from the centroidal logitudinal axis to the outer surface is

$$c = \frac{d}{2}$$
$$T = \frac{\tau_{\max} J}{c} = \frac{\pi \tau_{\max} d^3}{16}$$
$$d = \sqrt[3]{\frac{16T}{\pi \tau_{\max}}} = \sqrt[3]{\frac{(16)(358.1 \text{ N·m})}{\pi(55 \times 10^6 \text{ Pa})}} = 0.0321 \text{ m}$$

The angle of twist is

$$\phi = \frac{TL}{JG}$$
$$= \left(\frac{(358.1 \text{ N·m})(10 \text{ m})}{\left(\frac{\pi}{32} \right)(0.0321 \text{ m})^4(80 \times 10^9 \text{ Pa})} \right) \left(\frac{360°}{2\pi \text{ rad}} \right)$$
$$= 24.6° \quad (25°)$$

(This is far greater than would be permitted in practice.)

Answer is C.

54. A motor delivers 500 kW to the shaft and gear assembly shown. The shaft speed is 4 Hz, and gears A and B transmit 300 kW and 200 kW to their respective mechanisms. The allowable shear stress and the maximum angle of twist of the shaft are 60 MPa and 1°, respectively. The shear modulus of the shaft is 80 GPa.

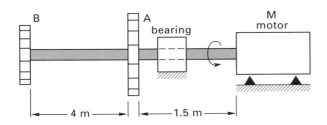

The minimum shaft diameter is most nearly

(A) 80 mm
(B) 120 mm
(C) 125 mm
(D) 145 mm

Solution:

The largest torque occurs in the shorter shaft section.

$$T_1 = \frac{P}{2\pi f} = \frac{500 \times 10^3 \text{ W}}{(2\pi)(4 \text{ Hz})} = 1.989 \times 10^4 \text{ N·m}$$

$$\tau = \frac{16T_1}{\pi d^3}$$

$$d = \sqrt[3]{\frac{16T_1}{\pi\tau}} = \sqrt[3]{\frac{(16)(1.989 \times 10^4 \text{ N·m})}{\pi(60 \times 10^6 \text{ Pa})}}$$

$$= 0.119 \text{ m} \quad (119 \text{ mm}) \quad \text{[as limited by torque]}$$

$$T_2 = \frac{200 \times 10^3 \text{ W}}{(2\pi)(4 \text{ Hz})} = 7.96 \times 10^3 \text{ N·m}$$

$$J = \left(\frac{\pi}{32}\right)d^4$$

$$\phi = \sum_{i=1}^{2} \frac{T_i L_i}{GJ_i}$$

$$= \left(\frac{32}{G\pi d^4}\right)\sum_{1}^{2} T_i L_i$$

$$\frac{(1°)(2\pi \text{ rad})}{360°} = \left(\frac{32}{(80 \times 10^9 \text{ Pa})\pi d^4}\right)$$
$$\times \left(\begin{array}{l}(1.989 \times 10^4 \text{ N·m})(1.5 \text{ m}) \\ + (7.96 \times 10^3 \text{ N·m})(0.4 \text{ m})\end{array}\right)$$

Solving for d,

$$d = 0.125 \text{ m} \quad (125 \text{ mm}) \quad \text{[as limited by twist]}$$

Twist is the limiting factor.

Answer is C.

55. The round cantilever beam ABC is stepped from $d_1 = 2$ cm to $d_2 = 1$ cm. The length of each section is 0.5 m, and the modulus of elasticity is 70 GPa.

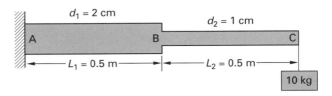

If a mass of 10 kg is supported at the free end, the deflection of the tip is most nearly

(A) 100 mm
(B) 140 mm
(C) 170 mm
(D) 200 mm

Solution:

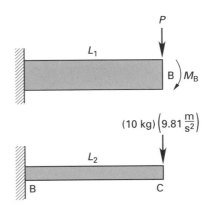

$$EI = (70 \times 10^9 \text{ Pa})\left(\frac{\pi}{4}\right)\left(\left(\frac{2 \text{ cm}}{2}\right)\left(\frac{1 \text{ m}}{100 \text{ cm}}\right)\right)^4$$

$$= 549.8 \text{ N·m}^2$$

The moment at B due to the mass is

$$M_B = (10 \text{ kg})\left(9.81 \frac{\text{m}}{\text{s}^2}\right)(0.5 \text{ m}) = 49.05 \text{ N·m}$$

The deflection at B is

$$\delta_B = \delta_{\text{due to force at B}} + \delta_{\text{due to moment at B}}$$

From the beam deflection equations,

$$\delta_B = \left(\frac{FL_1^2}{6EI}\right)(3L_1 - L_1) + \frac{M_B L_1^2}{2EI}$$

$$= \frac{(10 \text{ kg})\left(9.81 \frac{\text{m}}{\text{s}^2}\right)(0.5 \text{ m})^3}{(3)(549.8 \text{ N·m}^2)} + \frac{(49.05 \text{ N·m})(0.5)^2}{(2)(549.8 \text{ N·m}^2)}$$

$$= 0.0186 \text{ m}$$

The angle of deflection at B is

$$\phi_B = \phi_{\text{due to force}} + \phi_{\text{due to moment}}$$

$$= \frac{FL_1^2}{2EI} + \frac{M_B L_1}{EI}$$

$$= \frac{(10 \text{ kg})\left(9.81 \dfrac{\text{m}}{\text{s}^2}\right)(0.5 \text{ m})^2}{(2)(549.8 \text{ N·m}^2)} + \frac{(49.05 \text{ N·m})(0.5)}{549.8 \text{ N·m}}$$

$$= 0.0669 \text{ rad}$$

$$\delta_{\text{due to force at C}} = \frac{FL_2^3}{3EI_{BC}}$$

$$EI_{BC} = (70 \times 10^9 \text{ Pa})\left(\frac{\pi}{4}\right)\left(\left(\frac{1 \text{ cm}}{2}\right)\left(\frac{1 \text{ m}}{100 \text{ cm}}\right)\right)^4$$

$$= 34.36 \text{ N·m}^2$$

$$\delta_C = \delta_B + \theta_B L_2 + \delta_{\text{due to force at C}}$$

$$= 0.0186 \text{ m} + (0.0669 \text{ rad})(0.5 \text{ m})$$

$$+ \frac{(10 \text{ kg})\left(9.81 \dfrac{\text{m}}{\text{s}^2}\right)(0.5 \text{ m})^3}{(3)(34.36 \text{ N·m}^2)}$$

$$= 0.171 \text{ m} \quad (170 \text{ mm})$$

Answer is C.

THERMODYNAMICS

56. Air, which may be treated as an ideal gas, is compressed in a closed system from an initial state of 100 kPa and 300K to a pressure of 1500 kPa. The compression process is reversible and follows the relation $pv^{1.3} = C$. The work of compression is most nearly

(A) 200 kJ/kg
(B) 250 kJ/kg
(C) 265 kJ/kg
(D) 300 kJ/kg

Solution:

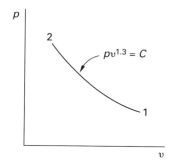

$$v_1 = \frac{RT_1}{p_1}$$

$$= \frac{\left(0.287 \dfrac{\text{kJ}}{\text{kg·K}}\right)(300\text{K})}{100 \text{ kPa}}$$

$$= 0.861 \text{ m}^3/\text{kg}$$

$$p_1 v_1^n = p_2 v_2^n$$

$$(100 \text{ kPa})\left(0.861 \dfrac{\text{m}^3}{\text{kg}}\right)^{1.3} = (1500 \text{ kPa})(v_2)^{1.3}$$

$$v_2 = 0.1072 \text{ m}^3/\text{kg}$$

The work is

$$W_{1-2} = \frac{p_2 v_2 - p_1 v_1}{n - 1}$$

$$= \frac{\begin{array}{c}(1500 \text{ kPa})\left(0.1072 \dfrac{\text{m}^3}{\text{kg}}\right) \\ - (100 \text{ kPa})\left(0.861 \dfrac{\text{m}^3}{\text{kg}}\right)\end{array}}{1.3 - 1}$$

$$= 249 \text{ kJ/kg} \quad (250 \text{ kJ/kg})$$

Answer is B.

57. Water at 1.0 MPa and 40°C ($h = 168 \text{ kJ/kg}$) enters an adiabatic desuperheater operating at steady state and mixes with 1000 kg/h of superheated steam entering at 1.0 MPa and 300°C. The resulting mixture leaves as saturated steam at 0.8 MPa.

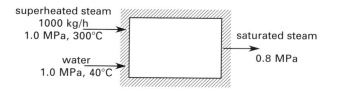

Assuming changes in kinetic and potential energies are negligible, the mass rate of flow of the water is most nearly

(A) 50 kg/h
(B) 80 kg/h
(C) 110 kg/h
(D) 140 kg/h

Solution:

The continuity equation is

$$\dot{m}_w + \dot{m}_{sh} = \dot{m}_s$$

(Subscripts w, sh, and s refer to water, superheated steam, and saturated steam, respectively.)

For this problem $\dot{Q}_{\text{in}}$, $\dot{W}_{\text{in}}$, KE, and PE are zero, so

$$\sum \dot{m}_i h_i = \sum \dot{m}_e h_e$$

Combining the continuity and energy equations,

$$\dot{m}_w h_w + \dot{m}_{sh} h_{sh} = (\dot{m}_{sh} + \dot{m}_w) h_s$$

Substituting values from steam tables gives

$$\dot{m}_w \left(168 \ \frac{\text{kJ}}{\text{kg}}\right) + \left(1000 \ \frac{\text{kg}}{\text{h}}\right) \left(3051.2 \ \frac{\text{kJ}}{\text{kg}}\right)$$

$$= \left(\dot{m}_w + 1000 \ \frac{\text{kg}}{\text{h}}\right) \left(2769.1 \ \frac{\text{kJ}}{\text{kg}}\right)$$

$$\dot{m}_w = 108.5 \ \text{kg/h} \quad (110 \ \text{kg/h})$$

Answer is C.

58. A Carnot engine using air as a working fluid develops 5 kW. The engine operates between two thermal reservoirs at 800K and 300K. If the volume doubles during the heat transfer to the engine, the mass flow rate of the air is most nearly

   (A) 0.02 kg/s
   (B) 0.05 kg/s
   (C) 0.10 kg/s
   (D) 0.13 kg/s

Solution:

$$\Delta s = R \ln \left(\frac{v_2}{v_1}\right) = \left(0.287 \ \frac{\text{kJ}}{\text{kg·K}}\right) \ln (2)$$

$$= 0.1989 \ \text{kJ/kg·K}$$

The power output is

$$P = \dot{m} Q = \dot{m} \Delta T \Delta s$$

$$\dot{m} = \frac{5 \ \text{kW}}{(800\text{K} - 300\text{K}) \left(0.1989 \ \frac{\text{kJ}}{\text{kg·K}}\right)}$$

$$= 0.0503 \ \text{kg/s} \quad (0.05 \ \text{kg/s})$$

Answer is B.

59. 1 kg of water is cooled from 90°C to the surrounding temperature of 20°C. Assuming the specific heat of water is 4.18 kJ/kg·K, the total change in entropy (system and surroundings) is most nearly

   (A) 0.05 kJ/K
   (B) 0.1 kJ/K
   (C) 0.9 kJ/K
   (D) 1.0 kJ/K

Solution:

$$Q = mc\Delta T$$

$$= (1 \ \text{kg}) \left(4.18 \ \frac{\text{kJ}}{\text{kg·K}}\right) (20°\text{C} - 90°\text{C})$$

$$= -292.6 \ \text{kJ}$$

$$\Delta S_{\text{system}} = mc \ln \left(\frac{T_2}{T_1}\right)$$

$$= (1 \ \text{kg}) \left(4.18 \ \frac{\text{kJ}}{\text{kg·K}}\right) \ln \left(\frac{20°\text{C} + 273}{90°\text{C} + 273}\right)$$

$$= -0.8955 \ \text{kJ/K}$$

$$\Delta S_{\text{surroundings}} = \frac{Q_{\text{surroundings}}}{T_{\text{surroundings}}} = \frac{292.6 \ \text{kJ}}{20°\text{C} + 273}$$

$$= 0.9986 \ \text{kJ/K}$$

$$\Delta S_{\text{total}} = -0.8955 \ \frac{\text{kJ}}{\text{K}} + 0.9986 \ \frac{\text{kJ}}{\text{K}}$$

$$= 0.1031 \ \text{kJ/K} \quad (0.1 \ \text{kJ/K})$$

Answer is B.

60. Air at 1 MPa and 400K expands through an adiabatic turbine operating at steady state to 0.15 MPa and 320K. Changes in kinetic and potential energies are negligible, and air can be assumed to be an ideal gas with constant specific heats. The surrounding temperature is 298.15K.

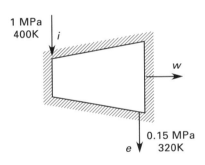

The reversible work that could have been developed if the expansion took place with the same inlet and exit states is most nearly

(A) 120 kJ/kg
(B) 150 kJ/kg
(C) 180 kJ/kg
(D) 210 kJ/kg

Solution:

$$w_{rev} = (h_e - h_i) - T_0(s_e - s_i)$$

$$= c_p(T_e - T_i) - T_0\left(c_p \ln\left(\frac{T_e}{T_i}\right) - R\ln\left(\frac{p_e}{p_i}\right)\right)$$

$$= \left(1.0035\ \frac{\text{kJ}}{\text{kg·K}}\right)(320\text{K} - 400\text{K})$$

$$- (298.15\text{K})\left(\begin{array}{l}\left(1.0035\ \frac{\text{kJ}}{\text{kg·K}}\right)\ln\left(\frac{320\text{K}}{400\text{K}}\right)\\[2mm] -\left(0.287\ \frac{\text{kJ}}{\text{kg·K}}\right)\ln\left(\frac{0.15\ \text{MPa}}{1\ \text{MPa}}\right)\end{array}\right)$$

$$= -175.85\ \text{kJ/kg} \quad (180\ \text{kJ/kg})$$

Answer is C.

61. Compressed air in a tank is at a pressure of 800 kPa and a temperature of 600K. Assuming air to be an ideal gas with constant specific heats, and assuming the temperature of the environment is 25°C, the closed-system availability exhausting to a standard atmospheric pressure is most nearly

(A) 85 kJ/kg
(B) 100 kJ/kg
(C) 112 kJ/kg
(D) 120 kJ/kg

Solution:

$$v = \frac{RT}{p} = \frac{\left(0.287\ \frac{\text{kJ}}{\text{kg·K}}\right)(600\text{K})}{800\ \text{kPa}}$$

$$= 0.21525\ \text{m}^3/\text{kg}$$

$$T_0 = 25°\text{C} + 273 = 298\text{K}$$

$$v_0 = \frac{RT_0}{p_0} = \frac{\left(0.287\ \frac{\text{kJ}}{\text{kg·K}}\right)(298\text{K})}{101.3\ \text{kPa}}$$

$$= 0.8443\ \text{m}^3/\text{kg}$$

The availability is

$$\phi - \phi_0 = (u - u_0) + p_0(v - v_0) - T_0(s - s_0)$$

$$= c_v(T - T_0) + p_0(v - v_0)$$

$$- T_0\left(c_p \ln\left(\frac{T}{T_0}\right) - R\ln\left(\frac{p}{p_0}\right)\right)$$

$$= \left(0.7165\ \frac{\text{kJ}}{\text{kg·K}}\right)(600\text{K} - 298\text{K})$$

$$+ (101.3\ \text{kPa})\left(0.21525\ \frac{\text{m}^3}{\text{kg}} - 0.8443\ \frac{\text{m}^3}{\text{kg}}\right)$$

$$- (298\text{K})\left(\begin{array}{l}\left(1.0035\ \frac{\text{kJ}}{\text{kg·K}}\right)\ln\left(\frac{600\text{K}}{298\text{K}}\right)\\[2mm] -\left(0.287\ \frac{\text{kJ}}{\text{kg·K}}\right)\ln\left(\frac{800\ \text{kPa}}{101.3\ \text{kPa}}\right)\end{array}\right)$$

$$= 120.1\ \text{kJ/kg}$$

Answer is D.

62. Benzene (C_6H_6) is burned with 20% excess air. The air-fuel ratio by mass is nearest to

(A) 12
(B) 16
(C) 18
(D) 20

Solution:

The stoichiometric reaction per volume of benzene is

$$C_6H_6(\ell) + 7.5O_2(g) + (7.5)(3.76)N_2(g) \longrightarrow$$
$$6CO_2(g) + 3H_2O(g) + (7.5)(3.76)N_2(g)$$

With 20% excess air,

$$C_6H_6(\ell) + (1.2)(7.5)O_2(g)$$
$$+ (1.2)(7.5)(3.76)N_2(g) \longrightarrow$$
$$6CO_2(g) + 3H_2O(g) + (1.2)(7.5)(3.76)N_2(g)$$
$$+ (0.2)(7.5)O_2(g)$$

$$C_6H_6(\ell) + 9O_2(g) + 33.84N_2(g) \longrightarrow$$
$$6CO_2(g) + 3H_2O(g) + 33.84N_2(g) + 1.5O_2(g)$$

The molecular weight of benzene is

$$(6)\left(12\ \frac{\text{kg}}{\text{kmol}}\right) + (6)\left(1\ \frac{\text{kg}}{\text{kmol}}\right) = 78\ \frac{\text{kg}}{\text{kmol}}$$

The mass air fuel ratio is

$$\frac{A}{F} = \frac{\begin{array}{c}(9 \text{ kmol}) \left(32 \dfrac{\text{kg}}{\text{kmol}}\right) \\ + (33.84 \text{ kmol}) \left(28 \dfrac{\text{kg}}{\text{kmol}}\right)\end{array}}{78 \dfrac{\text{kg}}{\text{kmol}}}$$

$$= 15.84 \text{ kg of air/kg of fuel} \quad (16)$$

Answer is B.

63. If the total pressure of the products in the reaction in Prob. 62 is atmospheric, the dew-point temperature is nearest to
    (A) 25°C
    (B) 28°C
    (C) 32°C
    (D) 39°C

Solution:

The mole fraction and partial pressure ratio are the same.

$$x_i = \frac{N_i}{N} = \frac{p_i}{p_{\text{total}}}$$

The partial pressure of water is

$$p_{\text{water}} = x_{\text{water}} p_{\text{total}}$$

$$= \left(\frac{3}{6 + 3 + 33.84 + 1.5}\right)(101.3 \text{ kPa})$$

$$= 6.854 \text{ kPa}$$

For this value of saturation pressure, steam tables give the dew point as

$$T_{\text{dp}} = 38.5°\text{C} \quad (39°\text{C})$$

Answer is D.

Practice Exam

1. What is the characteristic equation for the following block diagram?

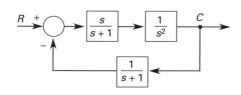

(A) $s^3 + s^2 + 1 = 0$
(B) $s^4 + s^2 + 1 = 0$
(C) $s^3 + 2s^2 + s + 1 = 0$
(D) $s^4 + 2s^3 + s^2 + s = 0$

2. A linear system is defined by the following differential equation.

$$\frac{dy}{dt} + 10y = 2$$

$$y(0) = 1$$

What are the poles of the system?

(A) $0, -10$
(B) $-2, 0$
(C) $2, 0$
(D) $10, 2$

3. The transfer function of a system is given by

$$P(s) = \frac{s+3}{(s+1)(s+2)}$$

The magnitude and phase of system frequency response, at the frequency $\omega = 1$ are

(A) $2, -63°$
(B) $1, -53°$
(C) $-1, +53°$
(D) $-2, +63°$

4. A program segment references a subroutine called "SUB1" as listed.

```
X = 3
Y = 1
CALL SUB1(X,Y,Z)
Z = Z + Z
PRINT Z
END
SUBROUTINE SUB1(X,Y,Z)
Z = SQRT(X*Y+X)
RETURN
END
```

The output of the program is most nearly

(A) 0.0
(B) 2.5
(C) 3.0
(D) 6.0

5. A compiler's function is to

(A) convert assembly code to a high level language
(B) execute a computer program
(C) convert a computer code to machine language
(D) debug a computer program

6. The data required by the following general program is entered by the user.

```
      ARRAY TAB(4)
      I = 1
      READ TAB(1 TO 4)
      SUM = 1
15    SUM = SUM + TAB(I)
      TAB(I) = SUM
      IF I = 4 GO TO 20
      I = I + 1
      GO TO 15
20    PRINT TAB(4)
      END
```

The array is loaded by the user as follows

```
TAB(1) = 1
TAB(2) = 2
TAB(3) = 3
TAB(4) = 4
```

The output of the program is most nearly

(A) 0
(B) 4
(C) 11
(D) 16

7. A 2 g bullet with velocity of 100 m/s strikes a 1000 g wooden block moving at a velocity of 10 m/s in the same direction as the bullet. The bullet imbeds itself in the block upon impact. The final velocity of the block is most nearly

(A) 5 m/s
(B) 10 m/s
(C) 15 m/s
(D) 20 m/s

8. A solid disk 4 m in diameter rolls on a horizontal surface as shown. At a particular instant, the angular velocity and acceleration of the disk are 10 rad/s (counterclockwise) and 3 rad/s^2 (clockwise), respectively.

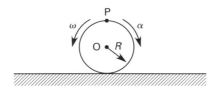

At this instant, the acceleration of point P located at the very top of the disk is most nearly

(A) 100 m/s^2
(B) 150 m/s^2
(C) 200 m/s^2
(D) 250 m/s^2

9. Two splined wheels of radius 20 cm and 50 cm are connected to a mass by a cable as shown. The cable is roped around the small wheel. The mass exerts a force of 200 N, which is large enough to cause the wheels to roll without slipping on the incline.

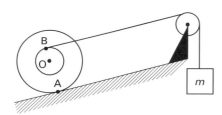

If the mass moves down by 10 cm, the displacement of the wheel is most nearly

(A) 5 cm
(B) 7 cm
(C) 10 cm
(D) 13 cm

10. A uniform disk of 10 kg mass and 0.5 m diameter rolls without slipping on a flat horizontal surface, as shown.

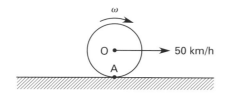

When its horizontal velocity is 50 km/h, the total kinetic energy of the disk is most nearly

(A) 1000 J
(B) 1200 J
(C) 1450 J
(D) 1600 J

11. A two-bar linkage rotates about the pivot point O as shown. The length of members AB and OA are 2.0 m and 2.5 m, respectively. The angular velocity and acceleration of member OA are $\omega_{OA} = 0.8$ rad/s counterclockwise and $\alpha_{OA} = 0$. The angular velocity of member AB is $\omega_{AB} = 1.2$ rad/s clockwise, and the acceleration of member AB is $\alpha_{AB} = 3$ rad/s^2 counterclockwise.

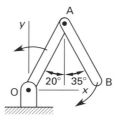

When the bars are in the position shown, the magnitude of the acceleration of point B (i.e., the tip) is most nearly

(A) 3 m/s^2
(B) 5 m/s^2
(C) 8 m/s^2
(D) 12 m/s^2

12. A flywheel with a center hub is used to lower a mass of 150 kg, as shown. The radius of the hub is 50 cm, and the mass moment of inertia of the combined flywheel and hub is 20 kg·m^2. All frictional losses are negligible. At a particular instant, the velocity of the mass is 3 m/s downward.

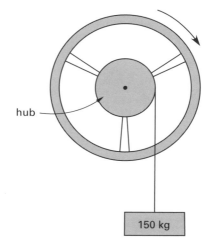

The velocity of the mass after 2 additional meters of travel is most nearly

(A) 4.5 m/s
(B) 6.0 m/s
(C) 9.5 m/s
(D) 14 m/s

13. Superheated steam at a pressure of 1.0 MPa and a temperature of 250°C enters the turbine of an ideal regenerative cycle with one feedwater heater. Steam is extracted at 0.2 MPa to heat the feedwater in an open heater. The rest of the steam expands to the condenser pressure of 10 kPa. Neglecting pump work, the mass of the extracted steam per kilogram of steam entering the turbine is most nearly

(A) 0.09 kg/kg
(B) 0.13 kg/kg
(C) 0.17 kg/kg
(D) 0.20 kg/kg

14. An air-standard diesel cycle has a compression ratio of 18 and a cutoff ratio of 2.2. At the beginning of the isentropic compression process, the temperature of the air is 310K. Assuming the ratio of specific heats is $k = 1.4$, the maximum temperature in the cycle is most nearly

(A) 1950K
(B) 2040K
(C) 2170K
(D) 2250K

15. The pressure ratio of an ideal air-standard gas turbine cycle is 7:1. Air enters the compressor at a temperature of 300K and a pressure of 95 kPa. The heat input to the cycle is 700 kJ/kg of air. Assuming constant specific heats, the thermal efficiency is most nearly

(A) 36%
(B) 43%
(C) 48%
(D) 50%

16. A pump is used to move water through a horizontal pipe at a rate of 0.03 m³/s. The pressure and diameter upstream of the pump are 150 kPa and 100 mm, respectively. The values downstream are 600 kPa and 50 mm, respectively. There are 200 J/kg of frictional losses in the system. The hydraulic efficiency of the pump is most nearly

(A) 70%
(B) 75%
(C) 80%
(D) 85%

17. A fan is used to move air through an air-conditioning duct at a rate of 2.8 m³/s. The system operating point for the fan, point 1 on the characteristic curve, is indicated. The required power is 1.5 kW. When the speed of the fan is increased to a certain value, it is noticed that the power requirement is tripled.

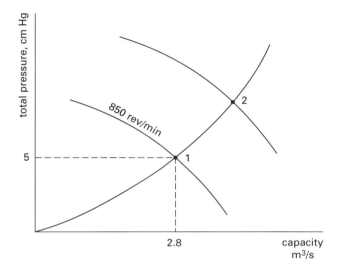

The ratio of the new fan capacity and the total pressure Q_2/p_2 is most nearly

(A) 0.1 m³/s·cm Hg
(B) 0.2 m³/s·cm Hg
(C) 0.3 m³/s·cm Hg
(D) 0.4 m³/s·cm Hg

18. Air enters a compressor at a pressure of 101 kPa and exits at a pressure of 800 kPa. The air velocity at the entrance is 2 m/s, and the volumetric flow rate is 5 kg/s. The losses are 10% of the required compressor work, and the increase in kinetic energy across the compressor is 10%. Assume the air density remains constant at 1.23 kg/m³. If the compressor efficiency is 85%, the power required by the compressor is most nearly

(A) 1.5 MW
(B) 3.0 MW
(C) 4.5 MW
(D) 6.0 MW

19. A vertical jet of water just supports a flat plate having a mass of 1.2 kg as shown. The nozzle diameter is 2 cm, and the water leaves the nozzle at a speed of 8.5 m/s.

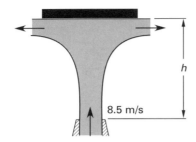

The vertical distance, h, is most nearly

(A) 2.2 m
(B) 2.7 m
(C) 3.4 m
(D) 4.0 m

20. Water flows through a smooth contraction as shown.

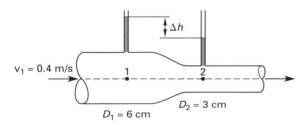

The difference in the fluid heights, Δh, is most nearly

(A) 0.08 m
(B) 0.10 m
(C) 0.12 m
(D) 0.15 m

21. Water flows steadily upward through a diverging tube. At section 1 the diameter is 2 cm, and the velocity is 2.5 m/s. At a subsequent section, the diameter is 8 cm.

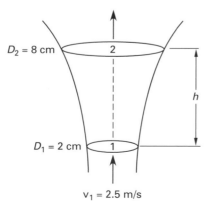

If the pressure remains constant, the axial distance between the two sections is most nearly

(A) 0.1 m
(B) 0.3 m
(C) 0.8 m
(D) 1.2 m

22. A tank having a uniform cross-sectional area of 3 m^2 contains water at 300K. The tank is open to the atmosphere. The water is drained through a 2 cm^2 hole in the bottom of the tank. The time it takes to completely drain the tank is most nearly

(A) 50 s
(B) 75 s
(C) 100 s
(D) 150 s

23. Air at 300K and 101.3 kPa and with a velocity of 22 m/s is flowing over a transverse cylinder 10 cm in diameter. If the kinematic viscosity of the air is 15.89×10^{-6} m^2/s, the drag force per unit length of the cylinder is most nearly

(A) 37 N
(B) 43 N
(C) 52 N
(D) 54 N

24. Water at 300K flows through a horizontal 1.5 mm diameter tube. The viscosity of the water is 855×10^{-6} N·s/m^2. What is the maximum pressure drop per meter length of tube such that flow remains laminar?

(A) 9 kPa
(B) 12 kPa
(C) 16 kPa
(D) 18 kPa

25. The temperature distribution across a 0.3 m thick wall at a certain moment is

$$T = 200 - 200x + 30x^2$$

T is in °C, and x is in meters measured from one side of the wall. The coefficient of thermal conductivity of the wall is 2 W/m·K. The net heat transfer to the wall per unit area is most nearly

(A) 27 W/m^2
(B) 31 W/m^2
(C) 36 W/m^2
(D) 43 W/m^2

26. A stainless steel tube (3 cm inside diameter and 5 cm outside diameter) is covered with 4 cm insulation. The thermal conductivities of steel and insulation are 20 W/m·K and 0.06 W/m·K, respectively. If the inside wall temperature of the tube is 500°C, and the outside temperature of the insulation is 50°C, what is the heat loss per meter of the tube?

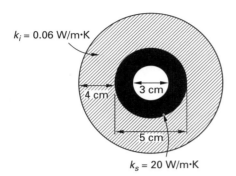

$k_i = 0.06$ W/m·K

4 cm   3 cm   5 cm

$k_s = 20$ W/m·K

(A) 120 W/m
(B) 140 W/m
(C) 160 W/m
(D) 180 W/m

27. A solid copper sphere 8 cm in diameter is initially at 400°C when it is suddenly exposed to air at 25°C. The average convective heat transfer coefficient is 25 W/m². The density, specific heat, and thermal conductivity of copper are 8933 kg/m³, 410 J/kg·K, and 380 W/m·K, respectively. What is the time required to cool the center of the sphere to 200°C?

(A) 12 min
(B) 16 min
(C) 20 min
(D) 25 min

28. Air at 300K flows at 0.45 m/s over a square flat plate 1 m on each side. The average kinematic viscosity of the air is 20.92×10^{-6} m²/s, the Prandtl number is 0.7, and the thermal conductivity is 30×10^{-3} W/m·K. If the surface temperature of the plate is 400K, the average heat transfer coefficient is most nearly

(A) 2.5 W/m²·K
(B) 5.0 W/m²·K
(C) 7.5 W/m²·K
(D) 8.2 W/m²·K

29. A counterflow heat exchanger is used to cool 0.1 kg/s of oil from 100°C to 70°C. Cooling water enters the heat exchanger at 30°C and leaves at 70°C. Assuming the specific heat of oil is 1.9 kJ/kg·K, and the overall heat transfer coefficient is 0.32 kW/m²·K, the heat exchanger area required is most nearly

(A) 0.1 m²
(B) 0.3 m²
(C) 0.5 m²
(D) 0.7 m²

30. Two plates of equal area are placed parallel to each other in a vacuum. One plate has an emmisivity of 0.2 and temperature of 700K, and the other plate has an emmisivity of 0.4 and a temperature of 500K. If the view factor is 0.8, the radiation heat flux will most nearly be

(A) 1.0 kW/m²
(B) 1.5 kW/m²
(C) 2.0 kW/m²
(D) 2.5 kW/m²

31. In a pearlitic SAE-1080 steel, the cementite platelets are 4×10^{-5} cm thick, and the ferrite platelets are 14×10^{-5} cm thick. The density of ferrite is 7.87 g/cm³, and the density of cementite is 7.66 g/cm³. The volume percentage of the cementite in the steel is most nearly

(A) 5%
(B) 8%
(C) 12%
(D) 18%

32. One-half of an eletrochemical cell consists of a pure nickel electrode in a 0.001 molal Ni^{2+} solution, and the other half is a cadmium electrode immersed in a 0.5 molal Cd^{2+} solution. The electrode potential is given by $E = E_0 + 0.0296 \log(c)$, where E_0 is the standard electrode potential and c is the molal concentration of the ions in the solution. The cell potential is most nearly

(A) −0.653 V
(B) −0.153 V
(C) −0.073 V
(D) +0.751 V

33. A 5 mm diameter rod is subjected to a 1.5 kN tensile load. The yield stress, modulus of elasticity, Poisson ratio, and length are 145 MPa, 70 GPa, 0.33, and 10 cm, respectively. The change in diameter of the rod is most nearly

(A) 0.002 mm
(B) 0.004 mm
(C) 0.008 mm
(D) 0.012 mm

34. From the data shown, the pressure difference between tanks A and B is most nearly

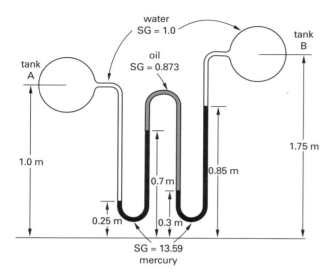

(A) 110 kPa
(B) 120 kPa
(C) 130 kPa
(D) 140 kPa

35. Water flows through a 10 cm inside diameter pipe as shown.

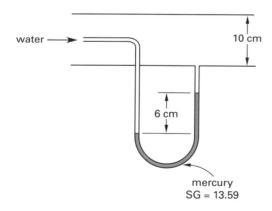

If the deflection of the manometer is 6 cm of mercury, the flow rate is most nearly

(A) 0.03 m³/s
(B) 0.05 m³/s
(C) 0.07 m³/s
(D) 0.09 m³/s

36. Water flows at a constant rate of 0.0045 m³/s through a horizontal venturi meter. The diameters at the inlet and throat are 10 cm and 3 cm, respectively. The difference in levels of the mercury columns of a differential manometer attached to the venturi meter is 20 cm. The discharge coefficient is most nearly

(A) 0.90
(B) 0.93
(C) 0.95
(D) 0.98

37. Water flows through an 8 cm inside diameter pipe at a constant rate of 0.03 m³/s. The water has a kinematic viscosity of 9.609×10^{-5} m²/s.

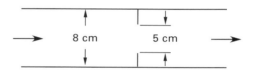

If a 5 cm diameter sharp-edged orifice plate is inserted in the pipe, the static pressure drop across the orifice is most nearly

(A) 200 kPa
(B) 260 kPa
(C) 310 kPa
(D) 380 kPa

38. Oil with a kinematic viscosity of 1120×10^{-6} m²/s flows at a velocity of 12.5 m/s in a 30 cm diameter pipe. To achieve dynamic similarity, a test is run using water at 17°C in a 2.5 cm diameter pipe. The velocity of the water should be most nearly

(A) 0.15 m/s
(B) 0.5 m/s
(C) 1.0 m/s
(D) 1.5 m/s

39. Air at a temperature of 320K flows at a supersonic speed in a wind tunnel. If the Mach number is 1.5, the velocity of air is most nearly

(A) 400 m/s
(B) 450 m/s
(C) 480 m/s
(D) 540 m/s

40. An aluminum tube is capped at two ends by two rigid plates. The plates are held in place by a steel bolt and a nut as shown. The pitch of the bolt is 2 mm, and its cross-sectional area is 2 cm². The cross-sectional area of the tube wall is 4 cm². After being snugly fit, the nut is turned a quarter of a turn, compressing the tube.

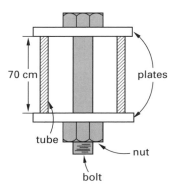

The stress in the bolt is most nearly

(A) 40 MPa
(B) 50 MPa
(C) 60 MPa
(D) 70 MPa

41. A bar of circular cross section is bent at both ends and loaded at the free ends as shown. The length and the diameter of the bar are 2 m and 6 cm, respectively, and the allowable tensile stress is 1.2 MPa.

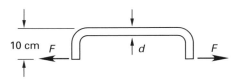

The maximum load that can safely be applied at the free end is most nearly

(A) 240 N
(B) 300 N
(C) 350 N
(D) 400 N

42. A pivoted shaft with solid circular cross section is suspended from a rigid surface as shown. The temperature of the shaft is increased 500°C, causing it to elongate. The thermal coefficient of expansion and modulus of elasticity are 15×10^{-6} 1/°C and 150 GPa, respectively.

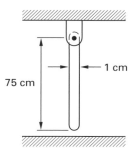

To avoid buckling of the shaft, the clearance between the free end of the shaft and the bottom surface should be most nearly

(A) 5.35 mm
(B) 5.45 mm
(C) 5.55 mm
(D) 5.60 mm

43. A rectangular steel plate is bolted to a rectangular column with four bolts as shown. A load of 20 kN is applied at the edge as shown.

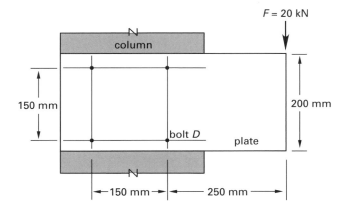

The resulting shear load on bolt D is most nearly

(A) 11 kN
(B) 15 kN
(C) 19 kN
(D) 20 kN

44. A hollow shaft is used to transmit 35 kW of power. The rotational speed is 1000 rev/min. The inside and outside diameters are 30 mm and 40 mm, respectively. The torsional shear stress developed in the shaft is most nearly

(A) 40 MPa
(B) 80 MPa
(C) 110 MPa
(D) 130 MPa

45. The plate shown has a concentric circular hole drilled through it. The plate is made from a brittle material whose ultimate stress is 1.5 MPa.

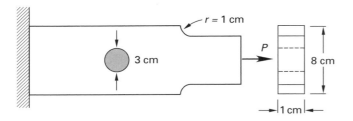

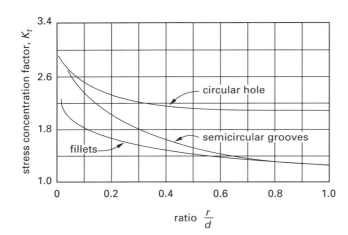

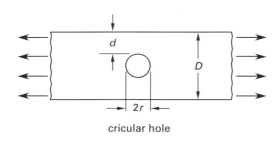

circular hole

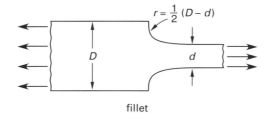

fillet

Using a factor of safety of 2.5 and the stress concentration diagram shown, the allowable tensile load is most nearly

(A)   115 N
(B)   135 N
(C)   150 N
(D)   165 N

46. A vapor-compression refrigeration cycle utilizes R-134a as a working fluid. The refrigerant enters the compressor as a saturated vapor at $-10°C$ and leaves the condenser as a saturated liquid at $40°C$. If the compressor efficiency is 80%, the work input to the compressor is most nearly

(A)   36 kJ/kg
(B)   42 kJ/kg
(C)   46 kJ/kg
(D)   52 kJ/kg

47. Refrigerant-134a at 0.8 MPa and $70°C$ is cooled and condensed at constant pressure in a steady-state process until it is a saturated liquid. Cooling water enters the condenser at $20°C$ and leaves at $30°C$. If the mass flow of the refrigerant is 0.1 kg/s, the mass flow rate of the cooling water is most nearly

(A)   0.50 kg/s
(B)   0.65 kg/s
(C)   0.70 kg/s
(D)   0.75 kg/s

48. A two-stage compression system together with the corresponding p-h diagram is shown.

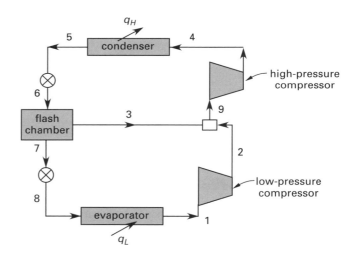

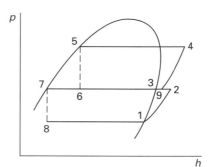

$$h_1 = 388.5 \text{ kJ/kg}$$
$$h_3 = 399.2 \text{ kJ/kg}$$
$$h_5 = h_6 = 243.7 \text{ kJ/kg}$$
$$h_7 = h_8 = 200.9 \text{ kJ/kg}$$

From the data given, the refrigeration load q_L per unit mass of fluid entering the condenser is most nearly

(A) 120 kJ/kg
(B) 135 kJ/kg
(C) 145 kJ/kg
(D) 160 kJ/kg

49. Member A in the truss shown is loaded axially at 30 kN. The allowable shear stress in member B is 600 kPa. Both members of the truss have the same width.

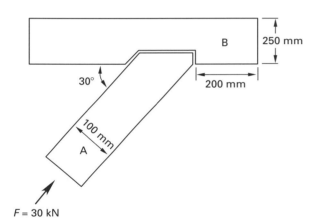

The width of member B to prevent shearing is most nearly

(A) 140 mm
(B) 170 mm
(C) 200 mm
(D) 220 mm

50. The truss shown is loaded at joint B with a vertical load of 90 kN. Both members of the truss have a cross-sectional area of 4 cm^2 and length of 1 m, and both are made of steel.

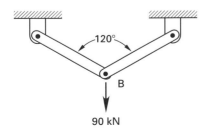

The vertical displacement of joint B is most nearly

(A) 1.0 mm
(B) 2.1 mm
(C) 3.3 mm
(D) 8.6 mm

51. An aluminum bar of length 60 cm is placed between two supports that are 60 cm apart. The supports are rigid and fixed and do not exert any initial stress on the bar. The bar is heated such that its temperature changes from 25°C to 100°C. The coefficient of thermal expansion of the aluminum is 23×10^{-6} 1/C°.

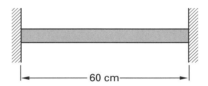

The stress developed at the supports is most nearly

(A) 70 MPa
(B) 120 MPa
(C) 170 MPa
(D) 250 MPa

52. A stepped solid circular shaft is subjected to torques T_1 and T_2, as shown. The shaft diameters (d_1 and d_2) are 80 mm and 60 mm, and the corresponding sectional lengths are 0.6 m and 0.4 m. The material is steel with a shear modulus of elasticity of 80 GPa.

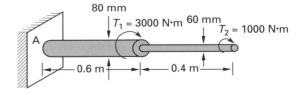

The angle of twist at the free end is most nearly

(A) 0.10°
(B) 0.20°
(C) 0.40°
(D) 0.66°

53. The cylindrical pressure vessel has an inside diameter of 2.5 m and a wall thickness of 15 mm. It is made of steel plates that are welded along a seam that makes an angle of 45° with the longitudinal axis. The internal pressure of the vessel is 8 MPa.

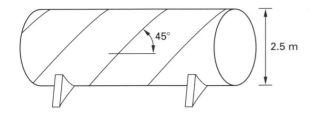

The normal component of the stress along the seam is most nearly

(A) 500 MPa
(B) 600 MPa
(C) 700 MPa
(D) 800 MPa

54. A cantilever beam with rectangular cross section is subjected to a 150 kN load as shown. The height and the width of the beam are 150 mm and 75 mm, respectively.

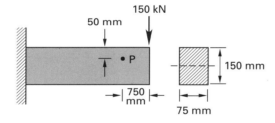

At the point P (50 mm from the top surface), the ratio of the magnitudes of the principal stresses (σ_1/σ_2) is most nearly

(A) 40
(B) 60
(C) 80
(D) 100

55. A rigid, thermally insulated vessel contains 1.0 kg of a water-vapor mixture at 100°C and a quality of 30%. An electric heater supplies energy to the vessel until the mixture becomes saturated vapor. The electric energy supplied is most nearly

(A) 1.0 MJ
(B) 1.2 MJ
(C) 1.5 MJ
(D) 1.6 MJ

56. A tank is connected to a supply manifold through a valve. The tank has a volume of 1 m³, and it initially contains air at 150 kPa and 300K. The air in the supply manifold has a pressure of 750 kPa and a temperature of 300K. The tank is uninsulated. The valve is opened and left open until the tank pressure stabilizes and the tank temperature returns to 300K.

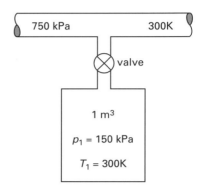

The heat transfer to the surroundings during the process is most nearly

(A) 100 kJ
(B) 150 kJ
(C) 450 kJ
(D) 600 kJ

57. A 5 kg block of copper initially at 200°C is placed in an insulated tank containing 10 kg of water at 25°C. The specific heat of copper and water are 0.39 kJ/kg·K and 4.18 kJ/kg·K, respectively. The total entropy generation is most nearly

(A) 0.23 kJ/K
(B) 0.30 kJ/K
(C) 0.35 kJ/K
(D) 0.38 kJ/K

58. Air is compressed adiabatically from 100 kPa and 25°C to 300 kPa in a steady-state operation. The work input to the compressor is 150 kJ/kg. Neglect changes in kinetic and potential energy, and assume air to be an ideal gas with constant specific heats. The net change in entropy per unit mass for the process is most nearly

(A) 0.02 kJ/kg·K
(B) 0.06 kJ/kg·K
(C) 0.09 kJ/kg·K
(D) 1.90 kJ/kg·K

59. A steady flow of air enters an adiabatic nozzle with negligible velocity at a pressure of 180 kPa and a temperature of 65°C. The mass flow rate is 1.0 kg/s, the exit pressure is 100 kPa, and the exit velocity is 300 m/s. The temperature of the environment is 10°C. The power lost due to irreversibility is most nearly

    (A) 6.7 kW
    (B) 7.4 kW
    (C) 8.5 kW
    (D) 9.2 kW

60. Air at a pressure of 1 atm, a temperature of 45°C, and a relative humidity of 10% enters an adiabatic humidifier operating at steady state. If the dry- and wet-bulb temperatures at the exit are 33.5°C and 31°C, respectively, the increase in the specific humidity is most nearly

    (A) 0.015 kg/kg
    (B) 0.019 kg/kg
    (C) 0.021 kg/kg
    (D) 0.022 kg/kg

SOLUTIONS FOR THE PRACTICE EXAM

1. Simplify the block diagram.

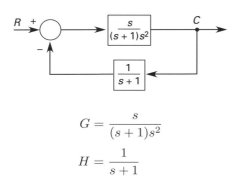

$$G = \frac{s}{(s+1)s^2}$$

$$H = \frac{1}{s+1}$$

The characteristic equation is

$$1 + GH = 0$$

$$1 + \left(\frac{s}{(s+1)s^2}\right)\left(\frac{1}{s+1}\right) = 0$$

$$s^2(s+1)^2 + s = 0$$

$$s^2(s^2 + 2s + 1) + s = 0$$

$$s^4 + 2s^3 + s^2 + s = 0$$

Answer is D.

2. The Laplace transform of the differential equation is

$$\mathcal{L}\left(\frac{dy}{dt}\right) + 10\mathcal{L}(y) = \mathcal{L}(2) \qquad \textit{Eq. 1}$$

$$\mathcal{L}\left(\frac{dy}{dt}\right) = sY(s) - y(0)$$

$$\mathcal{L}(y) = Y(s)$$

$$\mathcal{L}(2) = \frac{2}{s}$$

$$y(0) = 1$$

Substitute into Eq. 1.

$$sY(s) - 1 + 10Y(s) = \frac{2}{s}$$

$$(s+10)Y(s) = \frac{2}{s} + 1$$

$$Y(s) = \frac{\frac{s+2}{s}}{s+10} = \frac{s+2}{s(s+10)} \qquad \textit{Eq. 2}$$

The poles are the values that make the denominator of Eq. 2 zero.

$$s = 0, -10$$

Answer is A.

3. The angles are

$$\arctan\left(\tfrac{1}{3}\right) = 18.4°$$
$$\arctan\left(\tfrac{1}{2}\right) = 26.6°$$
$$\arctan\left(\tfrac{1}{1}\right) = 45°$$

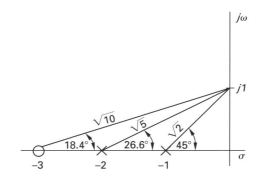

$$P(j1) = \frac{\sqrt{10}\underline{/18.4°}}{(\sqrt{5})(\sqrt{2})\underline{/45° + 26.6°}} = 1\underline{/-53.2°}$$

Answer is B.

4.
$$X = 3$$
$$Y = 1$$
$$Z = \sqrt{XY + X} = \sqrt{(3)(1) + 3}$$
$$\quad = 2.45$$
$$Z = Z + Z = 2.45 + 2.45$$
$$\quad = 4.9$$

Answer is D.

5. A compiler translates and converts high-level language code to machine code.

Answer is C.

6.
$$I = 1$$
SUM = 1
SUM = 1 + 1 = 2
TAB(1) = 2
SUM = 2 + 2 = 4
TAB(2) = 4
SUM = 4 + 3 = 7
TAB(3) = 7
SUM = 7 + 4 = 11
TAB(4) = 11

Answer is C.

7.

$$m_{\text{block}}v_{\text{block}} + m_{\text{bullet}}v_{\text{bullet}} = (m_{\text{block}} + m_{\text{bullet}})v_{\text{final}}$$

$$v_{\text{final}} = \frac{m_{\text{block}}v_{\text{block}} + m_{\text{bullet}}v_{\text{bullet}}}{m_{\text{block}} + m_{\text{bullet}}}$$

$$= \frac{(2\text{ g})\left(100\ \dfrac{\text{m}}{\text{s}}\right) + (1000\text{ g})\left(10\ \dfrac{\text{m}}{\text{s}}\right)}{2\text{ g} + 1000\text{ g}}$$

$$= 10.18\text{ m/s} \quad (10\text{ m/s})$$

Answer is B.

8.

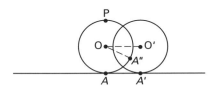

$$AA'' = R\theta$$

Let $AA' = AA'' = S = R\theta$. The linear displacement of the center O is

$$s = OO'$$

$$v_O = rw = (2\text{ m})\left(10\ \frac{\text{rad}}{\text{s}}\right) = 20\text{ m/s}$$

$$a_O = r\alpha = (2\text{ m})\left(3\ \frac{\text{rad}}{\text{s}^2}\right)$$

$$= 6\text{ m/s}^2 \quad [\text{to the right}]$$

$$v_P = v_{P/O} + v_O$$

$$v_{P/O} = (OP)\omega = (2\text{ m})\left(10\ \frac{\text{rad}}{\text{s}}\right) = 20\text{ m/s}$$

$$v_P = 20\ \frac{\text{m}}{\text{s}} + 20\ \frac{\text{m}}{\text{s}} = 40\text{ m/s} \quad [\text{to the left}]$$

$$a_P = \left(a_{P/O}\right)_t + \left(a_{P/O}\right)_n + a_O$$

$$\left(a_{P/O}\right)_t = (OP)\alpha = (2\text{ m})\left(3\ \frac{\text{rad}}{\text{s}^2}\right)$$

$$= 6\text{ m/s}^2 \quad [\text{to the right}]$$

$$\left(a_{P/O}\right)_n = (OP)\omega^2 = (2\text{ m})\left(10\ \frac{\text{rad}}{\text{s}}\right)^2$$

$$= 200\text{ m/s}^2 \quad [\text{downward}]$$

$$a_P = \sqrt{\left(6\ \frac{\text{m}}{\text{s}} + 6\ \frac{\text{m}}{\text{s}}\right)^2 + \left(200\ \frac{\text{m}}{\text{s}}\right)^2}$$

$$= 200.4\text{ m/s}^2 \quad (200\text{ m/s}^2)$$

Answer is C.

9. $$s_B = 10\text{ cm} = (R_1 + R_2)\theta$$

$$\theta = \frac{s_B}{R_1 + R_2} = \frac{10\text{ cm}}{20\text{ cm} + 50\text{ cm}} = 1/7\text{ rad}$$

The displacement of B relative to instant center A is

$$s_0 = R_2\theta = (50\text{ cm})\left(\frac{1}{7}\text{ rad}\right)$$

$$= 7.14\text{ cm} \quad (7\text{ cm})$$

Answer is B.

10.

$$v_0 = \left(50\ \frac{\text{km}}{\text{h}}\right)\left(1000\ \frac{\text{m}}{\text{km}}\right)\left(\frac{1}{3600}\ \frac{\text{h}}{\text{s}}\right) = 13.89\text{ m/s}$$

$$\text{angular speed} = \omega = \frac{v_0}{R} = \frac{13.89\ \dfrac{\text{m}}{\text{s}}}{\dfrac{0.5\text{ m}}{2}} = 55.56\text{ rad/s}$$

$$KE_{\text{total}} = KE_{\text{translation}} + KE_{\text{rotation}}$$

$$= \tfrac{1}{2}mv_0^2 + \tfrac{1}{2}I_0\omega^2 = \tfrac{1}{2}mv_0^2 + \tfrac{1}{2}\left(\tfrac{1}{2}mR^2\right)\omega^2$$

$$= \left(\frac{1}{2}\right)(10\text{ kg})\left(13.89\ \frac{\text{m}}{\text{s}}\right)^2$$

$$+ \left(\frac{1}{2}\right)\left(\left(\frac{1}{2}\right)(10\text{ kg})\left(\frac{0.5\text{ m}}{2}\right)^2\right)\left(55.56\ \frac{\text{rad}}{\text{s}}\right)^2$$

$$= 1447\text{ J} \quad (1450\text{ J})$$

Answer is C.

11.

$$\mathbf{a}_A = \omega_{OA} \times (\omega_{OA} \times \mathbf{r}_{A/O}) + (\boldsymbol{\alpha}_{OA} \times \mathbf{r}_{A/O})$$

$$= \left(0.8\mathbf{k}\ \frac{\text{rad}}{\text{s}}\right)$$

$$\times \left(\begin{array}{c}\left(0.8\mathbf{k}\ \dfrac{\text{rad}}{\text{s}}\right)\\ \times (2.5\ \text{m})(\mathbf{i}\sin 20° + \mathbf{j}\cos 20°)\end{array}\right) + 0$$

$$= -0.547\mathbf{i} - 1.504\mathbf{j} \quad [\text{toward O}]$$

$$\mathbf{a}_{B/A} = \omega_{AB} \times (\omega_{AB} \times \mathbf{r}_{B/A}) + (\boldsymbol{\alpha}_{AB} \times \mathbf{r}_{B/A})$$

$$= \left(-1.2\mathbf{k}\ \frac{\text{rad}}{\text{s}}\right)$$

$$\times \left(\begin{array}{c}\left(-1.2\mathbf{k}\ \dfrac{\text{rad}}{\text{s}}\right)\\ \times (2.0\ \text{m})(\mathbf{i}\sin 35° - \mathbf{j}\cos 35°)\end{array}\right)$$

$$= -1.6519\mathbf{i} + 2.3592\mathbf{j} + 3.4415\mathbf{j} + 4.591\mathbf{i}$$

$$= 3.263\mathbf{i} + 5.800\mathbf{j}$$

The acceleration of point B with respect to point O is

$$\mathbf{a}_B = \mathbf{a}_A + \mathbf{a}_{B/A}$$

$$= -0.547\mathbf{i} - 1.504\mathbf{j} + 3.263\mathbf{i} + 5.800\mathbf{j}$$

$$= 2.716\mathbf{i} + 4.296\mathbf{j}$$

$$|\mathbf{a}_B| = \sqrt{\left(2.716\ \frac{\text{m}}{\text{s}^2}\right)^2 + \left(4.296\ \frac{\text{m}}{\text{s}^2}\right)^2}$$

$$= 5.083\ \text{m/s}^2 \quad (5\ \text{m/s}^2)$$

Answer is B.

12.   The angular velocity is

$$\omega_1 = \frac{v_1}{R} = \frac{3\ \dfrac{\text{m}}{\text{s}}}{0.5\ \text{m}} = 6\ \text{rad/s}$$

$$E_1 = \tfrac{1}{2}mv_1^2 + \tfrac{1}{2}I\omega_1^2$$

$$= \left(\frac{1}{2}\right)(150\ \text{kg})\left(3\ \frac{\text{m}}{\text{s}}\right)^2$$

$$+ \left(\frac{1}{2}\right)(20\ \text{kg·m}^2)\left(6\ \frac{\text{rad}}{\text{s}}\right)^2$$

$$= 1035\ \text{J}$$

$$E_2 = \tfrac{1}{2}mv_2^2 + \tfrac{1}{2}I\omega_2^2$$

$$= \left(\frac{1}{2}\right)(150\ \text{kg})v_2^2 + \left(\frac{1}{2}\right)(20\ \text{kg·m}^2)\left(\frac{v_2}{0.5\ \text{m}}\right)^2$$

$$= (115\ \text{kg})v_2^2$$

From the principle of work and energy,

$$E_1 + {_1}W_2 = E_2$$

$$_1W_2 = F\Delta y = (150\ \text{kg})\left(9.81\ \frac{\text{m}}{\text{s}^2}\right)(2\ \text{m})$$

$$= 2943\ \text{J}$$

$$1035\ \text{J} + 2943\ \text{J} = (115\ \text{kg})v_2^2$$

$$v_2 = 5.88\ \text{m/s} \quad (6.0\ \text{m/s})$$

Answer is B.

13.

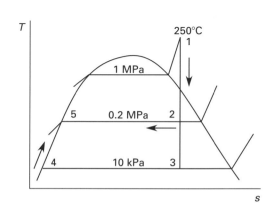

$$p_1 = 1\ \text{MPa}$$
$$T_1 = 250°\text{C}$$
$$h_1 = 2942.6\ \text{kJ/kg}$$
$$s_1 = 6.9247\ \text{kJ/kg·K}$$
$$p_2 = 0.2\ \text{MPa}$$
$$T_2 \approx 120°\text{C} \quad \left[\begin{array}{l}\text{use properties of saturated}\\ 120°\text{C water for convenience}\end{array}\right]$$
$$s_2 = s_1 = s_f + x_2 s_{fg}$$

$$x_2 = \frac{s_2 - s_f}{s_{fg}} = \frac{6.9247\ \dfrac{\text{kJ}}{\text{kg·K}} - 1.5276\ \dfrac{\text{kJ}}{\text{kg·K}}}{5.6020\ \dfrac{\text{kJ}}{\text{kg·K}}}$$

$$= 0.963$$

$$h_2 = h_f + x_2 h_{fg} = 503.71\ \frac{\text{kJ}}{\text{kg}} + (0.963)\left(2202.6\ \frac{\text{kJ}}{\text{kg}}\right)$$

$$= 2625\ \text{kJ/kg}$$

$$p_4 = 10\ \text{kPa} \quad \left[\begin{array}{l}\text{use properties of saturated}\\ 45°\text{C water for convenience}\end{array}\right]$$
$$h_4 = 188.45\ \text{kJ/kg}$$
$$p_5 = 0.2\ \text{MPa}$$
$$h_5 = h_f = 503.71\ \text{kJ/kg}$$

The energy balance equation for the heater is

$$mh_2 + (1-m)h_4 = h_5$$

$$m = \frac{h_5 - h_4}{h_2 - h_4} = \frac{503.71\ \dfrac{\text{kJ}}{\text{kg}} - 188.45\ \dfrac{\text{kJ}}{\text{kg}}}{2625\ \dfrac{\text{kJ}}{\text{kg}} - 188.45\ \dfrac{\text{kJ}}{\text{kg}}}$$

$$= 0.129\ \text{kg/kg}\quad (0.13\ \text{kg/kg})$$

Answer is B.

14.

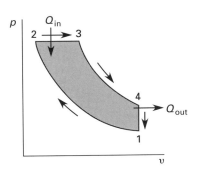

For the compression process,

$$\frac{T_2}{T_1} = \left(\frac{v_1}{v_2}\right)^{k-1}$$

The temperature at the end of the isentropic compression is

$$T_2 = T_1 \left(\frac{v_1}{v_2}\right)^{k-1} = (310\text{K})(18)^{1.4-1} = 985\text{K}$$

The temperature at the end of the combustion process is

$$T_3 = T_2 \left(\frac{v_3}{v_2}\right) = (985\text{K})(2.2) = 2167\text{K}\quad (2170\text{K})$$

Answer is C.

15.

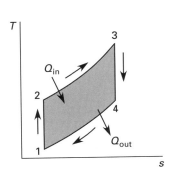

$$\frac{T_2}{T_1} = \left(\frac{p_2}{p_1}\right)^{\frac{k-1}{k}}$$

$$T_2 = (300\text{K})(7)^{\frac{1.4-1}{1.4}} = 523.1\text{K}$$

$$q_{2-3} = c_p(T_3 - T_2)$$

$$T_3 = \frac{q_{2-3}}{c_p} + T_2 = \frac{700\ \dfrac{\text{kJ}}{\text{kg}}}{1.0035\ \dfrac{\text{kJ}}{\text{kg·K}}} + 523.1\text{K}$$

$$= 1220.7\text{K}$$

$$\frac{T_4}{T_3} = \left(\frac{p_4}{p_3}\right)^{\frac{k-1}{k}}$$

$$T_4 = (1220.7\text{K})\left(\frac{1}{7}\right)^{\frac{1.4-1}{1.4}} = 700.1\text{K}$$

$$\eta = \frac{|W_{\text{actual}}|}{q_{\text{in}}} = \frac{c_p(T_3 - T_4) - c_p(T_2 - T_1)}{q_{\text{in}}}$$

$$= \frac{\left(1.0035\ \dfrac{\text{kJ}}{\text{kg·K}}\right)\left(\begin{array}{c}1220.7\text{K} - 700.1\text{K}\\ -\ 523.1\text{K} + 300\text{K}\end{array}\right)}{700\ \dfrac{\text{kJ}}{\text{kg}}}$$

$$= 0.4265\quad (43\%)$$

Answer is B.

16.

$$v_2 = \frac{Q}{A_2} = \frac{0.03\ \dfrac{\text{m}^3}{\text{s}}}{\left(\dfrac{\pi}{4}\right)(0.05\ \text{m})^2} = 15.28\ \text{m/s}$$

$$v_1 = \frac{v_2 A_2}{A_1} = \frac{v_2 D_2^2}{D_1^2} = \frac{\left(15.28\ \dfrac{\text{m}}{\text{s}}\right)(0.05\ \text{m})^2}{(0.1\ \text{m})^2}$$

$$= 3.82\ \text{m/s}$$

$$W = \frac{p_2 - p_1}{\rho} + \frac{v_2^2 - v_1^2}{2} + \text{loss}$$

$$= \frac{600 \times 10^3\ \text{Pa} - 150 \times 10^3\ \text{Pa}}{1000\ \dfrac{\text{kg}}{\text{m}^3}}$$

$$+ \frac{\left(15.28\ \dfrac{\text{m}}{\text{s}}\right)^2 - \left(3.82\ \dfrac{\text{m}}{\text{s}}\right)^2}{2} + 200\ \dfrac{\text{J}}{\text{kg}}$$

$$= 759.4\ \text{J/kg}$$

$$\eta = \frac{759.4\ \dfrac{\text{J}}{\text{kg}} - 200\ \dfrac{\text{J}}{\text{kg}}}{759.4\ \dfrac{\text{J}}{\text{kg}}} = 0.737\quad (75\%)$$

Answer is B.

17.

$$\frac{W_1}{W_2} = \left(\frac{n_1}{n_2}\right)^3 \qquad \text{Eq. 1}$$

$$\frac{\dot{Q}_1}{\dot{Q}_2} = \left(\frac{n_1}{n_2}\right) \qquad \text{Eq. 2}$$

$$\frac{p_1}{p_2} = \left(\frac{n_1}{n_2}\right)^2 \qquad \text{Eq. 3}$$

From Eq. 1,

$$\frac{n_1}{n_2} = \left(\frac{W_1}{W_2}\right)^{\frac{1}{3}} = \left(\frac{1}{3}\right)^{\frac{1}{3}}$$

$$n_2 = n_1 \left(\frac{1}{3}\right)^{-\frac{1}{3}} = \left(850 \ \frac{\text{rev}}{\text{min}}\right)\left(\frac{1}{3}\right)^{-\frac{1}{3}}$$

$$= 1226 \ \text{rev/min}$$

From Eq. 2,

$$Q_2 = \left(2.8 \ \frac{\text{m}^3}{\text{s}}\right)\left(\frac{1226 \ \frac{\text{rev}}{\text{min}}}{850 \ \frac{\text{rev}}{\text{min}}}\right) = 4.04 \ \text{m}^3/\text{s}$$

From Eq. 3,

$$p_2 = (5 \ \text{cm Hg})\left(\frac{1226 \ \frac{\text{rev}}{\text{min}}}{850 \ \frac{\text{rev}}{\text{min}}}\right)^2 = 10.4 \ \text{cm Hg}$$

$$\frac{Q_2}{p_2} = \frac{4.04 \ \frac{\text{m}^3}{\text{s}}}{10.4 \ \text{cm Hg}}$$

$$= 0.388 \ \text{m}^3/\text{s·cm Hg} \quad (0.4 \ \text{m}^3/\text{s·cm Hg})$$

Answer is D.

18.

$$\frac{p_2 - p_1}{\rho} + \frac{v_2^2 - v_1^2}{2} + g(z_2 - z_1) = W_{\text{comp}} + \text{loss}$$

$$\frac{800 \times 10^3 \ \text{Pa} - 101 \times 10^3 \ \text{Pa}}{1.23 \ \frac{\text{kg}}{\text{m}^3}} + \frac{(0.1)\left(2 \ \frac{\text{m}}{\text{s}}\right)^2}{2} + 0$$

$$= W_{\text{comp}} + (0.1)(W_{\text{comp}})$$

$$W_{\text{comp}} = 5.17 \times 10^5 \ \text{J/kg}$$

$$P_{\text{ideal}} = \dot{m} W_{\text{comp}} = \left(5 \ \frac{\text{kg}}{\text{s}}\right)\left(5.17 \times 10^5 \ \frac{\text{J}}{\text{kg}}\right)$$

$$= 2.58 \times 10^6 \ \text{W} \quad (2.58 \ \text{MW})$$

The required power is

$$P_{\text{actual}} = \frac{P_{\text{ideal}}}{\eta} = \frac{2.58 \ \text{MW}}{0.85}$$

$$= 3.04 \ \text{MW} \quad (3.0 \ \text{MW})$$

Answer is B.

19. The force on the plate is equal to its weight.

$$R_y = \dot{m}\text{v} = m_{\text{plate}}g$$

$$\text{v} = \frac{R_y}{\dot{m}} = \frac{m_{\text{plate}}g}{\rho A_0 \text{v}_0}$$

$$= \frac{(1.2 \ \text{kg})\left(9.81 \ \frac{\text{m}}{\text{s}^2}\right)}{\left(1000 \ \frac{\text{kg}}{\text{m}^3}\right)\left(\frac{\pi}{4}\right)(0.02 \ \text{m})^2 \left(8.5 \ \frac{\text{m}}{\text{s}}\right)}$$

$$= 4.41 \ \text{m/s}$$

From Bernoulli's equation,

$$\frac{p_0}{\rho g} + \frac{\text{v}_0^2}{2g} + z_0 = \frac{p}{\rho g} + \frac{\text{v}^2}{2g} + z$$

$$p_0 = p$$

$$z - z_0 = h$$

$$h = \frac{\text{v}_0^2 - \text{v}^2}{2g} = \frac{\left(8.5 \ \frac{\text{m}}{\text{s}}\right)^2 - \left(4.41 \ \frac{\text{m}}{\text{s}}\right)^2}{(2)\left(9.81 \ \frac{\text{m}}{\text{s}^2}\right)}$$

$$= 2.69 \ \text{m} \quad (2.7 \ \text{m})$$

Answer is B.

20. Bernoulli's equation is

$$\frac{p_1}{\rho g} + \frac{\text{v}_1^2}{2g} + z_1 = \frac{p_2}{\rho g} + \frac{\text{v}_2^2}{2g} + z_2$$

$$z_1 = z_2$$

$$\text{v}_2 = \text{v}_1\left(\frac{D_1^2}{D_2^2}\right) = \left(0.4 \ \frac{\text{m}}{\text{s}}\right)\left(\frac{6 \ \text{cm}}{3 \ \text{cm}}\right)^2 = 1.6 \ \text{m/s}$$

$$\Delta h = \frac{p_1 - p_2}{\rho g} = \frac{\text{v}_2^2 - \text{v}_1^2}{2g} = \frac{\left(1.6 \ \frac{\text{m}}{\text{s}}\right)^2 - \left(0.4 \ \frac{\text{m}}{\text{s}}\right)^2}{(2)\left(9.81 \ \frac{\text{m}}{\text{s}^2}\right)}$$

$$= 0.1223 \ \text{m} \quad (0.12 \ \text{m})$$

Answer is C.

21. Bernoulli's equation is

$$\frac{p_1}{\rho g} + \frac{v_1^2}{2g} + z_1 = \frac{p_2}{\rho g} + \frac{v_2^2}{2g} + z_2$$

However, $p_1 = p_2$, $z_2 - z_1 = h$, and

$$v_2 = \left(\frac{D_1}{D_2}\right)^2 v_1 = \left(\frac{2\ cm}{8\ cm}\right)^2 \left(2.5\ \frac{m}{s}\right)$$

$$= 0.1563\ m/s$$

$$h = z_2 - z_1 = \frac{v_1^2 - v_2^2}{2g} = \frac{\left(2.5\ \frac{m}{s}\right)^2 - \left(0.1563\ \frac{m}{s}\right)^2}{(2)\left(9.81\ \frac{m}{s^2}\right)}$$

$$= 0.3173\ m \quad (0.3\ m)$$

Answer is B.

22.

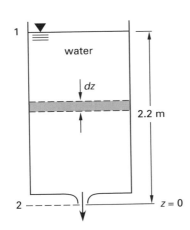

The exit velocity depends on the elevation z in the tank. Applying Bernoulli's equation between points 1 and 2 gives

$$\frac{p_1}{\rho g} + \frac{v_1^2}{2g} + z_1 = \frac{p_2}{\rho g} + \frac{v_2^2}{2g} + z_2$$

However, $p_1 = p_2$, $v_1 \approx 0$, and $z_2 = 0$, so

$$z = \frac{v_2^2}{2g}$$

$$v_2 = \sqrt{2gz}$$

$$Q = A_1\left(-\frac{dz}{dt}\right) = A_2 v_2 = A_2\sqrt{2gz}$$

Separating the variables and integrating gives

$$\int_0^t dt = -\int_{z=2.2}^0 \frac{A_1}{A_2}\left(\frac{dz}{\sqrt{2gz}}\right)$$

$$= \left(-\frac{A_1}{A_2\sqrt{2g}}\right)\left(\frac{\sqrt{z}}{\frac{1}{2}}\right)_{2.2\ m}^0$$

$$= \left(\frac{3\ m^2}{0.02\ m^2}\right)\left(\frac{\sqrt{2.2\ m}}{\frac{1}{2}\sqrt{(2)\left(9.81\ \frac{m}{s^2}\right)}}\right)$$

$$= 100.5\ s \quad (100\ s)$$

Answer is C.

23. To determine the drag coefficient, C_D, the Reynolds number must be determined.

$$Re = \frac{vD}{\nu} = \frac{\left(22\ \frac{m}{s}\right)(0.1\ m)}{15.89 \times 10^{-6}\ \frac{m^2}{s}}$$

$$= 13.8 \times 10^4$$

From a C_D versus Re graph for cylinders in cross flow, $C_D = 1.3$.

The density of air is

$$\rho = \frac{p}{RT} = \frac{(101.3\ kPa)\left(1000\ \frac{Pa}{kPa}\right)}{\left(287\ \frac{J}{kg\cdot K}\right)(300K)}$$

$$= 1.1766\ kg/m^3$$

The drag force per unit length is

$$F_D = C_D\rho\left(\frac{v^2}{2}\right)A \quad [A\ is\ the\ projected\ area.]$$

$$= (1.3)\left(1.1766\ \frac{kg}{m^3}\right)\left(\frac{\left(22\ \frac{m}{s}\right)^2}{2}\right)(0.1\ m)(1\ m)$$

$$= 37.0\ N \quad (37\ N)$$

Answer is A.

24. The maximum pressure drop corresponds to the maximum velocity in the tube, which in turn corresponds to the maximum value of Re for laminar flow.

$$\text{Re}_{max} = \frac{vD}{\nu} = 2300$$

$$\nu = \frac{\mu}{\rho} = \frac{855 \times 10^{-6} \; \frac{\text{N·s}}{\text{m}^2}}{1000 \; \frac{\text{kg}}{\text{m}^3}} = 0.855 \times 10^{-6} \; \text{m}^2/\text{s}$$

$$v = \text{Re}\left(\frac{\nu}{D}\right) = (2300)\left(\frac{0.855 \times 10^{-6} \; \frac{\text{m}^2}{\text{s}}}{0.0015 \; \text{m}}\right)$$

$$= 1.311 \; \text{m/s}$$

For laminar flow, use the Hagen-Poiseuille equation.

$$\Delta p = \frac{128\mu L Q}{\pi D^4} = \frac{32\mu L v}{D^2}$$

$$= \frac{(32)\left(855 \times 10^{-6} \; \frac{\text{N·s}}{\text{m}^2}\right)(1 \; \text{m})\left(1.311 \; \frac{\text{m}}{\text{s}}\right)}{(0.0015 \; \text{m})^2}$$

$$= 15.9 \times 10^3 \; \text{Pa} \quad (16 \; \text{kPa})$$

Answer is C.

25.

$$\frac{\partial T}{\partial x} = -200 + 60x$$

$$q''_{x=0} = -k \left.\frac{\partial T}{\partial x}\right|_{x=0}$$

$$= -\left(2 \; \frac{\text{W}}{\text{m·K}}\right)\left(-200 \; \frac{\text{K}}{\text{m}}\right)$$

$$= 400 \; \text{W/m}^2$$

$$q''_{x=0.3\,\text{m}} = -k \left.\frac{\partial T}{\partial x}\right|_{x=0.3\,\text{m}}$$

$$= -\left(2 \; \frac{\text{W}}{\text{m·K}}\right)\left(-200 \; \frac{\text{K}}{\text{m}} + \left(60 \; \frac{\text{K}}{\text{m}^2}\right)(0.3 \; \text{m})\right)$$

$$= 364 \; \text{W/m}^2$$

$$q''_{net} = 400 \; \frac{\text{W}}{\text{m}^2} - 364 \; \frac{\text{W}}{\text{m}^2} = 36 \; \text{W/m}^2$$

Answer is C.

26. The outer diameter of the insulation is

$$5 \; \text{cm} + 4 \; \text{cm} + 4 \; \text{cm} = 13 \; \text{cm}$$

$$\frac{\dot{Q}}{L} = \frac{2\pi(T_1 - T_3)}{\dfrac{\ln\left(\dfrac{r_2}{r_1}\right)}{k_s} + \dfrac{\ln\left(\dfrac{r_3}{r_2}\right)}{k_i}}$$

$$= \frac{(2\pi)(500\text{K} - 50\text{K})}{\dfrac{\ln\left(\dfrac{2.5 \; \text{cm}}{1.5 \; \text{cm}}\right)}{20 \; \dfrac{\text{W}}{\text{m·K}}} + \dfrac{\ln\left(\dfrac{6.5 \; \text{cm}}{2.5 \; \text{cm}}\right)}{0.06 \; \dfrac{\text{W}}{\text{m·K}}}}$$

$$= 177.3 \; \text{W/m} \quad (180 \; \text{W/m})$$

Answer is D.

27. The Biot number of a sphere is

$$\text{Bi} = \frac{hV}{kA_s} = \frac{h\frac{4}{3}\pi r^3}{k 4\pi r^2} = \frac{h\left(\dfrac{r}{3}\right)}{k}$$

$$= \frac{\left(25 \; \dfrac{\text{W}}{\text{m}^2 \cdot \text{K}}\right)\left(\dfrac{0.04 \; \text{m}}{3}\right)}{380 \; \dfrac{\text{W}}{\text{m·K}}}$$

$$= 0.00088$$

Since Bi < 0.1, the lumped capacitance method can be used.

$$T - T_\infty = (T_i - T_\infty)e^{-\left(\frac{hA_s}{\rho c_p V}\right)t}$$

$$\frac{T - T_\infty}{T_i - T_\infty} = e^{-\left(\frac{hA_s}{\rho c_p V}\right)t}$$

$$\ln\left(\frac{T - T_\infty}{T_i - T_\infty}\right) = -\frac{hA_s t}{\rho c_p V}$$

$$V = \frac{4}{3}\pi r^3 = \frac{\pi D^3}{6}$$

$$t = \left(\frac{\rho\left(\dfrac{\pi D^3}{6}\right)c_p}{h\pi D^2}\right)\ln\left(\frac{T_i - T_\infty}{T - T_\infty}\right)$$

$$= \left(\frac{\rho D c_p}{6h}\right)\ln\left(\frac{T_i - T_\infty}{T - T_\infty}\right)$$

$$= \left(\frac{\left(8933 \; \dfrac{\text{kg}}{\text{m}^3}\right)(0.08 \; \text{m})\left(410 \; \dfrac{\text{J}}{\text{kg·K}}\right)}{(6)\left(25 \; \dfrac{\text{W}}{\text{m}^2 \cdot \text{K}}\right)}\right)$$

$$\times \ln\left(\frac{400°\text{C} - 25°\text{C}}{200°\text{C} - 25°\text{C}}\right)\left(\frac{1}{60} \; \frac{\text{min}}{\text{s}}\right)$$

$$= 24.8 \; \text{min} \quad (25 \; \text{min})$$

Answer is D.

28. The maximum Reynolds number is

$$\text{Re}_L = \frac{\text{v}_\infty L}{\nu} = \frac{\left(0.45 \ \frac{\text{m}}{\text{s}}\right)(1 \ \text{m})}{20.92 \times 10^{-6} \ \frac{\text{m}^2}{\text{s}}} = 2.15 \times 10^4$$

Since Re_L is less than 10^5 the flow is laminar.

$$\text{Nu} = \frac{\overline{h}L}{k} = 0.648 \ \text{Re}_L^{\frac{1}{2}} \text{Pr}^{\frac{1}{3}}$$

$$= (0.648)(2.15 \times 10^4)^{\frac{1}{2}}(0.7)^{\frac{1}{3}}$$

$$= 84.36$$

$$\overline{h} = \text{Nu}\left(\frac{k}{L}\right) = (84.36)\left(\frac{30 \times 10^{-3} \ \frac{\text{W}}{\text{m·K}}}{1 \ \text{m}}\right)$$

$$= 2.53 \ \text{W/m}^2\text{·K} \quad (2.5 \ \text{W/m}^2\text{·K})$$

Answer is A.

29.

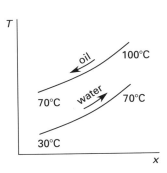

$$\dot{Q} = \dot{m}_\text{oil} c_{p_\text{oil}} \Delta T_\text{oil}$$

$$= \left(0.1 \ \frac{\text{kg}}{\text{s}}\right)\left(1.9 \ \frac{\text{kJ}}{\text{kg·K}}\right)(100°\text{C} - 70°\text{C})$$

$$= 5.7 \ \text{kW}$$

$$\Delta T_{\ell m} = \frac{(70°\text{C} - 30°\text{C}) - (100°\text{C} - 70°\text{C})}{\ln\left(\dfrac{70°\text{C} - 30°\text{C}}{100°\text{C} - 70°\text{C}}\right)}$$

$$= 34.76\text{K}$$

$$\dot{Q} = UA \ \Delta T_{\ell m}$$

$$5.7 \ \text{kW} = \left(0.32 \ \frac{\text{kW}}{\text{m}^2\text{·K}}\right)A(34.76\text{K})$$

$$A = 0.51 \ \text{m}^2 \quad (0.5 \ \text{m}^2)$$

Answer is C.

30.

$$\frac{\dot{Q}_{1-2}}{A} = \frac{\sigma(T_1^4 - T_2^4)}{\dfrac{1 - \epsilon_1}{\epsilon_1} + \dfrac{1}{F_{1-2}} + \dfrac{1 - \epsilon_2}{\epsilon_2}}$$

$$= \frac{\left(5.67 \times 10^{-8} \ \frac{\text{W}}{\text{m}^2\text{·K}^4}\right)((700\text{K})^4 - (500\text{K})^4)}{\dfrac{1 - 0.2}{0.2} + \dfrac{1}{0.8} + \dfrac{1 - 0.4}{0.4}}$$

$$= 1492 \ \text{W/m}^2 \quad (1.5 \ \text{kW/m}^2)$$

Answer is B.

31. SAE-1080 steel contains 0.8% carbon by weight. From the phase diagram in the *NCEES FE Reference Handbook*, the percentage of Fe_3C is

$$\text{wt\% Fe}_3\text{C} = \left(\frac{0.80\% - 0.02\%}{6.67\% - 0.02\%}\right)(100\%) = 11.73\%$$

$$\text{vol\% Fe}_3\text{C} = \left(\frac{\text{vol Fe}_3\text{C}}{\text{vol Fe}_3\text{C} + \text{vol cementite}}\right)(100\%)$$

$$= \left(\frac{\dfrac{m_{\text{Fe}_3\text{C}}}{\rho_{\text{Fe}_3\text{C}}}}{\dfrac{m_{\text{Fe}_3\text{C}}}{\rho_{\text{Fe}_3\text{C}}} + \dfrac{m_{\text{cementite}}}{\rho_{\text{cementite}}}}\right)(100\%)$$

$$= \left(\frac{(11.73\%)\left(\dfrac{1 \ \text{g}}{7.66 \ \frac{\text{g}}{\text{cm}^3}}\right)}{(11.73\%)\left(\dfrac{1 \ \text{g}}{7.66 \ \frac{\text{g}}{\text{cm}^3}}\right) + (88.27\%)\left(\dfrac{1 \ \text{g}}{7.87 \ \frac{\text{g}}{\text{cm}^3}}\right)}\right)(100\%)$$

$$= 0.1201 \quad (12\%)$$

Answer is C.

32.
$$\text{Cd} \longrightarrow \text{Cd}^{2+} + 2e^-$$
$$\text{Ni}^{2+} + 2e^- \longrightarrow N_i$$

$$E_{0,\text{Cd}} = -0.403 \ \text{V}$$

$$E_{0,\text{Ni}} = -0.250 \ \text{V}$$

$$E_\text{Cd} = -0.403 + (0.0296)\log(0.5) = -0.412 \ \text{V}$$

$$E_\text{Ni} = -0.250 + (0.0296)\log(0.001) = -0.339 \ \text{V}$$

Since E_{Cd} has the larger negative potential, Cd will corrode.

$$\Delta E = E_{Cd} - E_{Ni} = -0.412 \text{ V} - (-0.339 \text{ V}) = -0.073 \text{ V}$$

Answer is C.

33. $$\sigma = \frac{F}{A} = \frac{1.5 \times 10^3 \text{ N}}{\left(\frac{\pi}{4}\right)(0.005 \text{ m})^2} = 7.64 \times 10^7 \text{ Pa}$$

This is within the elastic range. The axial strain is

$$\epsilon_a = \frac{\sigma}{E} = \frac{7.64 \times 10^7 \text{ Pa}}{70 \times 10^9 \text{ Pa}} = 0.00109$$

The lateral strain is

$$\epsilon_\ell = \nu\epsilon_a = 0.33\epsilon_a = \frac{\Delta D}{D_0}$$

$$\Delta D = 0.33\epsilon_a D_0 = (0.33)(0.00109)(5 \text{ mm})$$
$$= 0.0018 \text{ mm} \quad (0.002 \text{ mm})$$

Answer is A.

34.

$$p_a + \gamma_w h_1 - \gamma_{Hg} h_2 + \gamma_{oil} h_3 - \gamma_{Hg} h_4 - \gamma_w h_5 = p_b$$

$h_1 = 1.0 \text{ m} - 0.25 \text{ m} = 0.75 \text{ m}$
$h_2 = 0.7 \text{ m} - 0.25 \text{ m} = 0.45 \text{ m}$
$h_3 = 0.7 \text{ m} - 0.3 \text{ m} = 0.4 \text{ m}$
$h_4 = 0.85 \text{ m} - 0.3 \text{ m} = 0.55 \text{ m}$
$h_5 = 1.75 \text{ m} - 0.85 \text{ m} = 0.90 \text{ m}$
$\gamma_w = \rho g$

$$p_a - p_b = \gamma_w(h_5 - h_1) + \gamma_{Hg}(h_2 + h_4) - \gamma_{oil} h_3$$

$$= \left(1000 \frac{\text{kg}}{\text{m}^3}\right)\left(9.81 \frac{\text{m}}{\text{s}^2}\right)$$

$$\times \left(\begin{array}{l} (0.90 \text{ m} - 0.75 \text{ m}) \\ + (13.59)(0.45 \text{ m} + 0.55 \text{ m}) \\ - (0.873)(0.4 \text{ m}) \end{array} \right)$$

$$= 1.314 \times 10^5 \text{ Pa} \quad (130 \text{ kPa})$$

Answer is C.

35. $$v_2 = \sqrt{2g\left(\frac{\rho_{Hg}}{\rho_w} - 1\right)h}$$

$$= \sqrt{(2)\left(9.81 \frac{\text{m}}{\text{s}^2}\right)\left(\frac{13.59}{1} - 1\right)(0.06 \text{ m})}$$

$$= 3.85 \text{ m/s}$$

$$Q = Av_2 = \left(\frac{\pi}{4}\right)(0.1 \text{ m})^2\left(3.85 \frac{\text{m}}{\text{s}}\right)$$

$$= 3.02 \times 10^{-2} \text{ m}^3/\text{s} \quad (0.03 \text{ m}^3/\text{s})$$

Answer is A.

36. $$\Delta p = (\rho_{Hg} - \rho_w)gh = \rho_w(SG_{Hg} - 1)gh$$

$$\frac{\Delta p}{\rho_w g} = (13.59 - 1)(0.2 \text{ m}) = 2.518 \text{ m}$$

$$Q = C_d A_t \sqrt{\frac{2g\left(\frac{\Delta p}{\rho_w g}\right)}{1 - \left(\frac{A_t}{A}\right)^2}}$$

$$= C_d\left(\frac{\pi}{4}\right)D_t^2\sqrt{\frac{2g\left(\frac{\Delta p}{\rho_w g}\right)}{1 - \left(\frac{D_t}{D}\right)^4}}$$

$$0.0045 \frac{\text{m}^3}{\text{s}} = C_d\left(\frac{\pi}{4}\right)(0.03 \text{ m})^2$$

$$\times \sqrt{\frac{(2)\left(9.81 \frac{\text{m}}{\text{s}^2}\right)(2.518 \text{ m})}{1 - \left(\frac{0.03 \text{ m}}{0.10 \text{ m}}\right)^4}}$$

$$C_d = 0.902 \quad (0.90)$$

Answer is A.

37. $$v = \frac{Q}{\frac{\pi}{4}D^2} = \frac{0.03 \frac{\text{m}^3}{\text{s}}}{\left(\frac{\pi}{4}\right)(0.08 \text{ m})^2} = 5.968 \text{ m/s}$$

$$\text{Re} = \frac{vD}{\nu} = \frac{\left(5.968 \frac{\text{m}}{\text{s}}\right)(0.08 \text{ m})}{9.609 \times 10^{-5} \frac{\text{m}^2}{\text{s}}}$$

$$= 4969 \quad [\text{turbulent}]$$

From the *NCEES FE Reference Handbook*, $C = 0.61$.

$$Q = CA\sqrt{\frac{2\Delta p}{\rho}}$$

$$0.03 \frac{\text{m}^3}{\text{s}} = (0.61)\left(\frac{\pi}{4}\right)(0.05 \text{ m})^2\sqrt{\frac{2\Delta p}{1000 \frac{\text{kg}}{\text{m}^3}}}$$

$$\Delta p = 313.6 \times 10^3 \text{ Pa} \quad (310 \text{ kPa})$$

Answer is C.

38. For dynamic similarity, the two Reynolds numbers must be the same.

$$\text{Re} = \frac{D\text{v}}{\nu}$$

$$\text{Re}_{\text{oil}} = \text{Re}_{\text{water}}$$

$$\frac{(0.30\text{ m})\left(12.5\,\dfrac{\text{m}}{\text{s}}\right)}{1120\times10^{-6}\,\dfrac{\text{m}^2}{\text{s}}} = \frac{(0.025\text{ m})\text{v}_{\text{water}}}{1.08\times10^{-6}\,\dfrac{\text{m}^2}{\text{s}}}$$

$$\text{v}_{\text{water}} = 0.145\text{ m/s}\quad(0.15\text{ m/s})$$

Answer is A.

39.
$$M = \frac{\text{v}}{c}$$

$$\text{v} = Mc = M\sqrt{kRT}$$

$$= (1.5)\sqrt{(1.4)\left(287\,\frac{\text{J}}{\text{kg·K}}\right)(320\text{K})}$$

$$= 537.9\text{ m/s}\quad(540\text{ m/s})$$

Answer is D.

40.
$$A_{\text{tube}} = \frac{4\text{ cm}^2}{\left(100\,\dfrac{\text{cm}}{\text{m}}\right)^2} = 4\times10^{-4}\text{ m}^2$$

$$A_{\text{bolt}} = \frac{2\text{ cm}^2}{\left(100\,\dfrac{\text{cm}}{\text{m}}\right)^2} = 2\times10^{-4}\text{ m}^2$$

The thread pitch is $h = 2$ mm. The displacement of the bolt relative to the tube, is

$$\delta_{\text{rel}} = \delta_{\text{bolt}} - \delta_{\text{tube}} = \frac{h}{4} \qquad \textit{Eq. 1}$$

$$\delta_{\text{tube}} = \frac{F_{\text{tube}}L_{\text{tube}}}{A_{\text{tube}}E_{\text{tube}}} \qquad \textit{Eq. 2}$$

$$\delta_{\text{bolt}} = \frac{F_{\text{bolt}}L_{\text{bolt}}}{A_{\text{bolt}}E_{\text{bolt}}} \qquad \textit{Eq. 3}$$

Combine Eqs. 1, 2, and 3.

$$\frac{h}{4} = \frac{F_{\text{bolt}}L_{\text{bolt}}}{A_{\text{bolt}}E_{\text{bolt}}} + \frac{F_{\text{tube}}L_{\text{tube}}}{A_{\text{tube}}E_{\text{tube}}}$$

Since there are no external forces,

$$-F_{\text{tube}} = F_{\text{bolt}}\quad\text{[tube in compression, bolt in tension]}$$

Solve for F_{bolt}.

$$F_{\text{bolt}} = \frac{\dfrac{h}{4}}{\dfrac{L_{\text{bolt}}}{A_{\text{bolt}}E_{\text{bolt}}} + \dfrac{L_{\text{tube}}}{A_{\text{tube}}E_{\text{tube}}}}$$

$$= \frac{\dfrac{0.002\text{ m}}{4}}{\dfrac{0.7\text{ m}}{(2\times10^{-4}\text{ m}^2)(205\times10^9\text{ Pa})} + \dfrac{0.7\text{ m}}{(4\times10^{-4}\text{ m}^2)(70\times10^9\text{ Pa})}}$$

$$= 11\,884\text{ N}$$

The stress in the bolt is

$$\sigma = \frac{F}{A} = \frac{11\,884\text{ N}}{(2\text{ cm}^2)\left(\dfrac{1}{100}\,\dfrac{\text{m}}{\text{cm}}\right)^2}$$

$$= 5.94\times10^7\text{ Pa}\quad(60\text{ MPa})$$

Answer is C.

41.

$$M = Fd = F(0.1\text{ m})$$

$$I = \left(\frac{\pi}{4}\right)R^4 = \left(\frac{\pi}{4}\right)\left(\frac{0.06\text{ m}}{2}\right)^4$$

$$= 6.36\times10^{-7}\text{ m}^4$$

$$\sigma = \frac{F}{A} + \frac{Mc}{I}$$

$$1.2\times10^6\text{ Pa} = \frac{F}{\left(\dfrac{\pi}{4}\right)(0.06\text{ m})^2} + \frac{(0.1F\text{ m})\left(\dfrac{0.06\text{ m}}{2}\right)}{6.36\times10^{-7}\text{ m}^4}$$

$$F = 236.7\text{ N}\quad(240\text{ N})$$

Answer is A.

42. The elongation due to temperature is

$$\delta_T = \alpha \Delta T L$$
$$= \left(15 \times 10^{-6} \frac{1}{\text{°C}}\right)(500\text{°C})(0.75 \text{ m})$$
$$= 0.00563 \text{ m} \quad (5.63 \text{ mm})$$

$$P_{\text{cr}} = \frac{\pi^2 EI}{k^2 \ell^2} = \frac{\pi^2 (150 \times 10^9 \text{ Pa})\left(\frac{\pi}{64}\right)(0.01 \text{ m})^4}{(1.0)^2(0.75 \text{ m})^2}$$
$$= 1292 \text{ N}$$

$$\delta_{\text{comp}} = \frac{PL}{EA} = \frac{(1292 \text{ N})(0.75 \text{ m})}{(150 \times 10^9 \text{ Pa})\left(\frac{\pi}{4}\right)(0.01 \text{ m})^2}$$
$$= 8.23 \times 10^{-5} \text{ m} \quad (0.0823 \text{ mm})$$

$$\delta = \delta_T - \delta_{\text{comp}} = 5.63 \text{ mm} - 0.0823 \text{ mm}$$
$$= 5.55 \text{ mm}$$

Answer is C.

43. The moment at the centroid of the bolt group is

$$M = Fd = (20 \text{ kN})\left(0.25 \text{ m} + \frac{0.15 \text{ m}}{2}\right)$$
$$= 6.5 \text{ kN·m}$$

The distance from the centroid to the center of each bolt is

$$r = \sqrt{(75 \text{ mm})^2 + (75 \text{ mm})^2} = 106 \text{ mm} \quad (0.106 \text{ m})$$

The shear load per critical bolt is the sum of the direct and torsional shears.

The direct shear per bolt is

$$V_{F,y} = \frac{F}{4} = \frac{20 \text{ kN}}{4} = 5 \text{ kN} \quad [\text{vertical}]$$

The torsional shear per bolt is

$$V_M = \frac{M}{4r} = \frac{6.5 \text{ kN·m}}{(4)(0.106 \text{ m})} = 15.33 \text{ kN}$$

The torsional shear is perpendicular to a line directed from the centroid of the bolt group to the bolt. For bolt D, the vertical and horiontal components are

$$V_{M,y} = V_M \sin 45° = (15.33 \text{ kN})(\sin 45°)$$
$$= 10.84 \text{ kN}$$
$$V_{M,x} = 10.84 \text{ kN}$$

The resultant shear on the bolt is

$$V = \sqrt{(V_{F,y} + V_{M,y})^2 + V_{M,x}^2}$$
$$= \sqrt{(5 \text{ kN} + 10.84 \text{ kN})^2 + (10.84 \text{ kN})^2}$$
$$= 19.2 \text{ kN}$$

Answer is C.

44.

$$J = \left(\frac{\pi}{32}\right)(d_o^4 - d_i^4) = \left(\frac{\pi}{32}\right)((40 \text{ mm})^4 - (30 \text{ mm})^4)$$
$$= 1.718 \times 10^5 \text{ mm}^4 \quad (1.718 \times 10^{-7} \text{ m}^4)$$

$$P = T\omega = 2\pi T \left(\frac{n}{60 \frac{\text{s}}{\text{min}}}\right)$$

$$T = \frac{\left(60 \frac{\text{s}}{\text{min}}\right)(35 \times 10^3 \text{ W})}{2\pi \left(1000 \frac{\text{rev}}{\text{min}}\right)} = 334.2 \text{ N·m}$$

$$\tau = \frac{Tc}{J} = \frac{(334.2 \text{ N·m})\left(\frac{40 \times 10^{-3} \text{ m}}{2}\right)}{1.718 \times 10^{-7} \text{ m}^4}$$
$$= 3.89 \times 10^7 \text{ N/m}^2 \quad (40 \text{ MPa})$$

Answer is A.

45. The allowable force is

$$P = \frac{\sigma_{\text{max}} A_{\text{net}}}{(\text{FS})K_t}$$

From the stress concentration factor diagram,

hole: $K_t \approx 2.0$ at $r/d = \dfrac{(3 \text{ cm})(2)}{(2)(8 \text{ cm} - 3 \text{ cm})} = 0.6$

fillet: $K_t \approx 1.7$ at $r/d = \dfrac{1 \text{ cm}}{8 \text{ cm} - (2)(1 \text{ cm})} = 0.17$

hole: $P = \dfrac{(1.5 \times 10^6 \text{ Pa})(0.01 \text{ m})(0.05 \text{ m})}{(2.5)(2.0)} = 150 \text{ N}$

fillet: $P = \dfrac{(1.5 \times 10^6 \text{ Pa})(0.01 \text{ m})(0.06 \text{ m})}{(2.5)(1.7)} = 212 \text{ N}$

$$P = 150 \text{ N} \quad [\text{limited by the hole}]$$

Answer is C.

46.

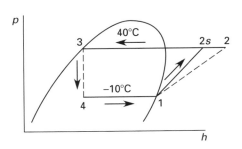

The efficiency of the compressor is

$$\eta_{\rm comp} = \frac{h_{2s} - h_1}{h_2 - h_1}$$

From R-134a tables or the p-h diagram, at $-10°C$,

$$h_1 = 392.9 \text{ kJ/kg}$$
$$s_1 = 1.7341 \text{ kJ/kg·K}$$

At 40°C,

$$p_{\rm sat} = 1.017 \text{ MPa}$$

$s_{2s} = s_1 = 1.7341$ kJ/kg·K and $p_{2s} = 1.017$ MPa,

$$h_{2s} \approx 426.4 \text{ kJ/kg·K}$$

$$W = h_2 - h_1 = \frac{h_{2s} - h_1}{\eta_{\rm comp}} = \frac{426.4 \frac{\text{kJ}}{\text{kg}} - 392.9 \frac{\text{kJ}}{\text{kg}}}{0.8}$$
$$= 41.88 \text{ kJ/kg} \quad (42 \text{ kJ/kg})$$

Answer is B.

47. The inlet and exit enthalpies are found from R-134a tables.

At 0.8 MPa and 70°C: $h_i = 455.3$ kJ/kg
At 0.8 MPa: $h_e = 243.7$ kJ/kg   [sat]

The inlet and exit enthalpies of water are found from steam tables.

At 20°C: $h_i = 83.96$ kJ/kg   [sat]
At 30°C: $h_e = 125.79$ kJ/kg   [sat]

The energy balance is

$$\dot{m}_{\rm R\text{-}134}(h_i - h_e)_{\rm R\text{-}134} = \dot{m}_{\rm water}(h_e - h_i)_{\rm water}$$

$$\left(0.1 \frac{\text{kg}}{\text{s}}\right)\left(455.3 \frac{\text{kJ}}{\text{kg}} - 243.7 \frac{\text{kJ}}{\text{kg}}\right)$$
$$= \dot{m}_{\rm water}\left(125.79 \frac{\text{kJ}}{\text{kg}} - 83.96 \frac{\text{kJ}}{\text{kg}}\right)$$
$$\dot{m}_{\rm water} = 0.506 \text{ kg/s} \quad (0.50 \text{ kg/s})$$

Answer is A.

48. Let x_6 represent the quality at state 6.

$$h_6 = h_7 + x_6(h_3 - h_7)$$

$$x_6 = \frac{h_6 - h_7}{h_3 - h_7} = \frac{243.7 \frac{\text{kJ}}{\text{kg}} - 200.9 \frac{\text{kJ}}{\text{kg}}}{399.2 \frac{\text{kJ}}{\text{kg}} - 200.9 \frac{\text{kJ}}{\text{kg}}} = 0.2158$$

$$q_L = (1 - x_6)(h_1 - h_8)$$
$$= (1 - 0.2158)\left(388.5 \frac{\text{kJ}}{\text{kg}} - 200.9 \frac{\text{kJ}}{\text{kg}}\right)$$
$$= 147.1 \text{ kJ/kg} \quad (145 \text{ kJ/kg}) \quad \text{[entering condenser]}$$

Answer is C.

49. The horizontal component of the force is

$$F_h = F\cos 30° = (30 \text{ kN})\cos 30° = 25.98 \text{ kN}$$

The shear area required is

$$A_s = \frac{F_h}{S_{\rm allowable}} = \frac{25.98 \text{ kN}}{600 \text{ kPa}}$$
$$= 0.0433 \text{ m}^2 \quad (43\,300 \text{ mm}^2)$$

The required width is

$$w = \frac{A_s}{200 \text{ mm}} = \frac{43\,300 \text{ mm}^2}{200 \text{ mm}} = 217 \text{ mm} \quad (220 \text{ mm})$$

Answer is D.

50. The force along each bar is

$$F_b = \frac{F}{2\cos 60°} = \frac{90 \text{ kN}}{(2)(0.5)} = 90 \text{ kN}$$

The strain energy of the two bars is

$$U = (2)\left(\frac{F_b^2 L}{2EA}\right)$$

The work done by the load is equal to the strain energy.

$$W = \frac{F_b \delta_B}{2} = U$$

$$\delta_B = \frac{2F_b L}{EA}$$

$$= \frac{(2)(90 \times 10^3 \text{ N})(1 \text{ m})}{(210 \times 10^9 \text{ Pa})(4 \text{ cm}^2)\left(\dfrac{1 \text{ m}^2}{10^4 \text{ cm}^2}\right)(0.5)^2}$$

$$= 8.57 \times 10^{-3} \text{ m} \quad (8.6 \text{ mm})$$

Answer is D.

51. The thermal elongation equals the mechanical compression.

$$0 = \alpha \Delta T L + \frac{FL}{AE}$$

$$\sigma = \frac{F}{A} = -\alpha \Delta T E$$

$$= -\left(23 \times 10^{-6} \frac{1}{°\text{C}}\right)(100°\text{C} - 25°\text{C})(70 \times 10^9 \text{ Pa})$$

$$= -1.21 \times 10^8 \text{ Pa} \quad (120 \text{ MPa}) \quad \text{[compressive]}$$

Answer is B.

52.

$$T = T_1 + T_2 = 3000 \text{ N·m} + 1000 \text{ N·m} = 4000 \text{ N·m}$$

$$\phi_1 = \frac{TL_1}{GJ_1} = \frac{TL_1}{G\left(\dfrac{\pi}{32}\right)d^4}$$

$$= \frac{(4000 \text{ N·m})(0.6 \text{ m})}{(80 \times 10^9 \text{ Pa})\left(\dfrac{\pi}{32}\right)(0.08 \text{ m})^4}$$

$$= 0.0075 \text{ rad} \quad (0.43°)$$

$$\phi_2 = \frac{T_2 L_2}{GJ_2}$$

$$= \frac{(1000 \text{ N·m})(0.4 \text{ m})}{(80 \times 10^9 \text{ Pa})\left(\dfrac{\pi}{32}\right)(0.06 \text{ m})^4}$$

$$= 0.0039 \text{ rad} \quad (0.23°)$$

The total twist is

$$\phi = \phi_1 + \phi_2 = 0.43° + 0.23° = 0.66°$$

Answer is D.

53.

$$\sigma_1 = \frac{pr}{t} = \frac{(8 \text{ MPa})(1.25 \text{ m})}{0.015 \text{ m}} = 666.67 \text{ MPa}$$

$$\sigma_2 = \frac{pr}{2t} = \frac{\sigma_1}{2} = \frac{666.67 \text{ MPa}}{2} = 333.33 \text{ MPa}$$

$$\sigma_x = \sigma_2 = 333.33 \text{ MPa}$$

The normal stress along the seam is

$$\sigma_{x'} = \frac{\sigma_x + \sigma_y}{2} + \left(\frac{\sigma_x - \sigma_y}{2}\right)\cos 2\theta + \tau_{xy}\sin 2\theta$$

$$\tau_{xy} = 0$$

$$\theta = 90° + 45° = 135°$$

$$\sigma_{x'} = \frac{666.67 \text{ MPa} + 333.33 \text{ MPa}}{2}$$

$$+ \left(\frac{\sigma_x - \sigma_y}{2}\right)(0) + 0$$

$$= 500 \text{ MPa}$$

Answer is A.

54.

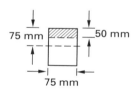

$$I = \frac{bh^3}{12} = \frac{(0.075 \text{ m})(0.15 \text{ m})^3}{12} = 2.11 \times 10^{-5} \text{ m}^4$$

$$M_P = Fd = (150 \text{ kN})(0.75 \text{ m}) = 112.5 \text{ kN·m}$$

The distance from the neutral axis to P is

$$y = 0.075 \text{ m} - 0.05 \text{ m} = 0.025 \text{ m}$$

$$\sigma_x = \frac{My}{I}$$

$$= \frac{(112.5 \times 10^3 \text{ kN·m})(0.025 \text{ m})}{2.11 \times 10^{-5} \text{ m}^4}$$

$$= 1.333 \times 10^8 \text{ Pa} \quad (133.3 \text{ MPa})$$

The shear force is

$$V = 150 \text{ kN}$$

The first moment of the shaded area about the neutral axis is Q.

$$\tau = \frac{VQ}{Ib} = \tau_{xy}$$

$$= \frac{(150 \times 10^3 \text{ N})(0.075 \text{ m})(0.05 \text{ m})(0.05 \text{ m})}{(2.11 \times 10^{-5} \text{ m}^4)(0.075 \text{ m})}$$

$$= 1.777 \times 10^7 \text{ Pa} \quad (17.77 \text{ MPa})$$

$$\tan 2\theta = \frac{2\tau_{xy}}{\sigma_x - \sigma_y} = \frac{(2)(17.77 \text{ MPa})}{133.3 \text{ MPa} - 0} = 0.267$$

$$2\theta = \tan^{-1}(0.267) = 14.93° \text{ or } 194.93°$$

$$\sigma_{x_1} = \frac{\sigma_x + \sigma_y}{2} + \left(\frac{\sigma_x - \sigma_y}{2}\right)\cos 2\theta$$
$$+ \tau_{xy}\sin 2\theta$$

For $2\theta = 14.93°$,

$$\sigma_{x_1} = \frac{133.3 \text{ MPa} + 0}{2} + \left(\frac{133.3 \text{ MPa} - 0}{2}\right)$$
$$\times \cos 14.93° + (17.77 \text{ MPa})\sin 14.93°$$
$$= 135.6 \text{ MPa}$$

For $2\theta = 194.93°$,

$$\frac{133.3 \text{ MPa} + 0}{2}$$
$$+ \left(\frac{133.3 \text{ MPa} - 0}{2}\right)\cos 194.93°$$
$$+ (17.77 \text{ MPa})\sin 194.93° = -2.33 \text{ MPa}$$

$$\left|\begin{matrix}\sigma_1 \\ \sigma_2\end{matrix}\right| = \left|\begin{matrix}\tau_{x_1} \\ \tau_{x_2}\end{matrix}\right| = \left|\frac{135.6 \text{ MPa}}{-2.33 \text{ MPa}}\right| = 58.2 \quad (60)$$

Answer is B.

55. The initial enthalpy at $100°$C is

$$h_1 = h_f + xh_{fg}$$
$$= 419.04 \frac{\text{kJ}}{\text{kg}} + (0.3)\left(2257.0 \frac{\text{kJ}}{\text{kg}}\right)$$
$$= 1096.1 \text{ kJ/kg}$$

The volume of the rigid container is

$$V = V_{\text{liquid}} + V_{\text{vapor}}$$
$$= m\big((1-x)v_f + xv_g\big)$$
$$= (1 \text{ kg})\left(\begin{matrix}(1-0.3)\left(0.001044 \frac{\text{m}^3}{\text{kg}}\right) \\ + (0.3)\left(1.6729 \frac{\text{m}^3}{\text{kg}}\right)\end{matrix}\right)$$
$$= 0.5026 \text{ m}^3$$

When all of the liquid has been vaporized, the specific volume will be

$$v_{g,2} = \frac{V}{m} = \frac{0.5026 \text{ m}^3}{1 \text{ kg}} = 0.5026 \text{ m}^3/\text{kg}$$

Use the steam tables for this value of v_g:

$$T_2 \approx 140°\text{C}$$
$$h_{g,2} = 2733.9 \text{ kJ/kg}$$

Energy required:

$$m(h_{g,2} - h_1) = (1 \text{ kg})\left(2733.9 \frac{\text{kJ}}{\text{kg}} - 1096.1 \frac{\text{kJ}}{\text{kg}}\right)$$
$$= 1637.8 \text{ kJ/kg} \quad (1.6 \text{ MJ})$$

Notice that energy is required to raise the pressure as well as the temperature, in addition to changing the phase. Enthalpy ($h = u + \rho v$) accounts for all of these factors.

Answer is D.

56. $$m_1 = \frac{p_1 V_1}{RT_1} = \frac{(150 \times 10^3 \text{ Pa})(1 \text{ m}^3)}{\left(287 \frac{\text{J}}{\text{kg·K}}\right)(300\text{K})} = 1.74 \text{ kg}$$

$$m_2 = \frac{p_2 V_2}{RT_2} = \frac{(750 \times 10^3 \text{ Pa})(1 \text{ m}^3)}{\left(287 \frac{\text{J}}{\text{kg·K}}\right)(300\text{K})} = 8.71 \text{ kg}$$

$$m_{\text{entering}} = m_2 - m_1 = 8.71 \text{ kg} - 1.74 \text{ kg}$$
$$= 6.97 \text{ kg}$$

The first law for this unsteady flow process is

$$Q + m_{\text{in}}h_{\text{in}} = m_2 u_2 - m_1 u_1$$

Substituting in the first law and assuming air to be an ideal gas,

$$Q = m_{\text{in}}c_p T_{\text{in}} + m_2 c_v T_2 - m_1 c_v T_1$$
$$= -(6.97 \text{ kg})\left(1.0035 \frac{\text{kJ}}{\text{kg·K}}\right)(300\text{K})$$
$$+ (8.71 \text{ kg})\left(0.7165 \frac{\text{kJ}}{\text{kg·K}}\right)(300\text{K})$$
$$- (1.74 \text{ kg})\left(0.7165 \frac{\text{kJ}}{\text{kg·K}}\right)(300\text{K})$$
$$= -600 \text{ kJ} \quad [\text{to the surroundings}]$$

Answer is D.

57. The energy balance equation gives

$$m_{\text{Cu}}c_{\text{Cu}}\Delta T_{\text{Cu}} = -m_{\text{water}}c_{\text{water}}\Delta T_{\text{water}}$$

$$(5 \text{ kg})\left(0.39 \frac{\text{kJ}}{\text{kg·K}}\right)(T_f - 200°\text{C})$$

$$= -(10 \text{ kg})\left(4.18 \frac{\text{kJ}}{\text{kg·K}}\right)(T_f - 25°\text{C})$$

$$T_f = 32.8°\text{C}$$

$$\Delta S_{\text{Cu}} = m_{\text{Cu}}c_{\text{Cu}}\ln\left(\frac{T_f}{T_i}\right)_{\text{Cu}}$$

$$= (5 \text{ kg})\left(0.39 \frac{\text{kJ}}{\text{kg·K}}\right)\ln\left(\frac{273 + 32.8°\text{C}}{273 + 200°\text{C}}\right)$$

$$= -0.8505 \text{ kJ/K}$$

$$\Delta S_{\text{water}} = m_{\text{water}}c_{\text{water}}\ln\left(\frac{T_f}{T_i}\right)_{\text{water}}$$

$$= (10 \text{ kg})\left(4.18 \frac{\text{kJ}}{\text{kg·K}}\right)\ln\left(\frac{273 + 32.8°\text{C}}{273 + 25°\text{C}}\right)$$

$$= 1.0800 \text{ kJ/K}$$

$$S_{\text{generated}} = -0.8505 \frac{\text{kJ}}{\text{K}} + 1.0800 \frac{\text{kJ}}{\text{K}}$$

$$= 0.2295 \text{ kJ/K} \quad (0.23 \text{ kJ/K})$$

Answer is A.

58. For an ideal gas in an adiabatic process with no change in kinetic and potential energies,

$$w_{\text{in}} = h_e - h_i = c_p(T_e - T_i)$$

$$150 \frac{\text{kJ}}{\text{kg}} = \left(1.0035 \frac{\text{kJ}}{\text{kg·°C}}\right)(T_e - 25°\text{C})$$

$$T_e = 174.5°\text{C}$$

The change of entropy per unit mass for the process is

$$\Delta s = c_p\ln\left(\frac{T_e}{T_i}\right) - R\ln\left(\frac{p_e}{p_i}\right)$$

$$= \left(1.0035 \frac{\text{kJ}}{\text{kg·K}}\right)\ln\left(\frac{273 + 174.5°\text{C}}{273 + 25°\text{C}}\right)$$

$$- \left(0.287 \frac{\text{kJ}}{\text{kg·K}}\right)\ln\left(\frac{300 \text{ kPa}}{100 \text{ kPa}}\right)$$

$$= 0.0927 \text{ kJ/kg·K} \quad (0.09 \text{ kJ/kg·K})$$

Answer is C.

59.

$$h_i = h_e + \frac{v_e^2}{2}$$

Assuming air to be an ideal gas,

$$c_p(T_i - T_e) = \frac{v_e^2}{2}$$

$$\left(1003.5 \frac{\text{J}}{\text{kg·K}}\right)(65°\text{C} - T_e) = \frac{\left(300 \frac{\text{m}}{\text{s}}\right)^2}{2}$$

$$T_e = 20.2°\text{C}$$

$$\dot{I} = \dot{m}T_0\Delta s = \left(1 \frac{\text{kg}}{\text{s}}\right)(273 + 10°\text{C})$$

$$\times \left(\begin{array}{c}\left(1.0035 \frac{\text{kJ}}{\text{kg·K}}\right)\ln\left(\frac{273 + 20.2°\text{C}}{273 + 65°\text{C}}\right) \\ - \left(0.287 \frac{\text{kJ}}{\text{kg·K}}\right)\ln\left(\frac{100 \text{ kPa}}{180 \text{ kPa}}\right)\end{array}\right)$$

$$= 7.36 \text{ kW} \quad (7.4 \text{ kW})$$

Answer is B.

60. From the psychrometric chart at $T_1 = 45°\text{C}$ and $\phi_1 = 10\%$,

$$\omega_1 = 0.006 \frac{\text{kg water}}{\text{kg dry air}}$$

At $T_{\text{db}} = 33.5°\text{C}$ and $T_{\text{wb}} = 31°\text{C}$,

$$\omega_2 = 0.028 \frac{\text{kg water}}{\text{kg dry air}}$$

The increase in specific humidity is

$$\omega_2 - \omega_1 = 0.028 \frac{\text{kg vapor}}{\text{kg dry air}} - 0.006 \frac{\text{kg vapor}}{\text{kg dry air}}$$

$$= 0.022 \text{ kg vapor/kg dry air}$$

Answer is D.

More FE/EIT Exam Practice!

All FE/EIT examinees take the same general exam in the morning session. To prepare for this four-hour test, you can use any of the following publications, depending on how much and what kind of review you need.

EIT Review Manual
Rapid Preparation for the General Fundamentals of Engineering Exam
Michael R. Lindeburg, PE
Paperback

The *EIT Review Manual* prepares you for the FE/EIT exam in the fastest, most efficient way possible. Updated to reflect the new exam content and format, this book gives you diagnostic tests to see what you need to study most, concise reviews of all exam topics, 1500+ practice problems with solutions, a complete eight-hour sample exam, and FE/EIT quiz software on diskette for your PC. The *EIT Review Manual* is your best choice if you are still in college or a recent graduate, or if your study time is limited.

Engineer-In-Training Reference Manual
Michael R. Lindeburg, PE
Hardcover

The "Big Yellow Book" has been helping engineers pass the FE/EIT exam for more than 20 years. A tried-and-true review, it provides in-depth coverage of subjects typically found in undergraduate engineering programs, focusing especially on those included on the FE/EIT exam. Thousands of formulas, tables, and illustrations plus more than 900 practice problems make the *Engineer-In-Training Reference Manual* the most comprehensive study manual you can buy—and an ideal choice if you have been out of school for a while.

Engineer-In-Training Sample Examinations
Michael R. Lindeburg, PE
Paperback

Most examinees benefit by taking a practice run through the FE/EIT exam before sitting down for the real thing. This book contains two full-length practice exams, including detailed solutions to all the problems. Each of these eight-hour tests has typical morning and general afternoon questions in multiple-choice format. Working these sample exams is a great way to get extra practice for the FE/EIT exam.

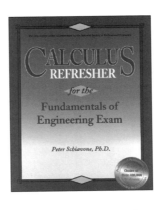

Calculus Refresher for the Fundamentals of Engineering Exam
Peter Schiavone, PhD
Paperback

Many engineers report having more trouble with problems involving calculus than with anything else on the FE/EIT exam. This book covers all the areas that you'll need to know for the exam: differential and integral calculus, centroids and moments of inertia, differential equations, and precalculus topics such as quadratic equations and trigonometry. You get clear explanations of theory, relevant examples, and FE-style practice problems (with solutions). If you are at all unsure of your calculus skills, this book is a must.

To order: 1-800-426-1178 or www.ppi2pass.com

BUSINESS REPLY MAIL

FIRST CLASS MAIL   PERMIT NO. 33   BELMONT, CA

POSTAGE WILL BE PAID BY ADDRESSEE

PROFESSIONAL PUBLICATIONS INC
1250 FIFTH AVE
BELMONT CA 94002-9979

NO POSTAGE
NECESSARY
IF MAILED
IN THE
UNITED STATES

BUSINESS REPLY MAIL

FIRST CLASS MAIL   PERMIT NO. 33   BELMONT, CA

POSTAGE WILL BE PAID BY ADDRESSEE

PROFESSIONAL PUBLICATIONS INC
1250 FIFTH AVE
BELMONT CA 94002-9979

NO POSTAGE
NECESSARY
IF MAILED
IN THE
UNITED STATES